ANIMAL FAMILIES

ANIMAL FAMILIES

by

MAURICE BURTON

Illustrated by Jane Burton

Routledge & Kegan Paul
LONDON

First published in 1958
by Routledge & Kegan Paul Ltd.
Broadway House, 68-74 Carter Lane
London E.C.4
Printed in Great Britain
by Latimer, Trend & Co. Ltd., Plymouth

CONTENTS

INTRODUCTION	1
BLACKBIRDS	3
PHEASANTS AND DUCKS	19
DANGERS IN THE AIR	37
HEDGEHOGS	49
SMALL AND LARGE FAMILIES	59
BABIES IN LIVING CRADLES	77
CROCODILES AND FROGS AS NURSEMAIDS	92
DEVOTED FISH FATHERS	103
MOSTLY ABOUT SPIDERS	121
INSECT SUPER-FAMILIES	134
INDEX	153

ILLUSTRATIONS

Nestling blackbirds gape upwards before their eyes are open *page* 11
Fledgling blackbirds gape at any moving object 17
Mother pheasant, feigning injury, leads the enemy away from her chicks 24
Half-grown young moorhen fetches parent to deal with disobedient younger brother 34
Father bullfinch raises head of dying chick to try to make it feed 40
Hen woodcock flies away with her chick held between her legs 46
Mother hedgehog carries her baby by its scruff 56
Father fox runs to his family with as much meat as his mouth will hold 62
Young fox-cubs taking food from the vixen 65
A lamb can get up and walk an hour after birth 69
The sloth provides a living cradle for her youngster 80
Baby opossums cling to mother's back to be carried about 83
The mother kangaroo carries her baby in a pouch 89
Do mother vipers swallow their young to protect them? 96
The surinam toad carries her family in pockets on her back 101

Illustrations

Male stickleback dances to attract the female and lead her to the nest to lay her eggs *page* 110
Male lumpsucker removing periwinkle which might crawl over the eggs which he is guarding in the crevice beside him 114
Cichlid parents with their newly-hatched young 119
Female wolf-spider carries her family pick-a-back 125
Baby spiders on nursery web crowd together in a ball 128
Queen ants climb to the top of a post escorted by workers, before setting off on their wedding flight 137
Hunting wasp dragging caterpillar to the burrow where she will lay her egg 145

INTRODUCTION

NO ANIMAL has a family life as complete as we know it. In the human family both parents share in looking after the children, and the children themselves are of different ages. This last is important because of the effect on the children themselves. When the first child is born, both parents can give it all their attention. When brothers and sisters arrive, less attention can be given to each by the parents. But nobody is the worse for that, for in such a family the younger children learn from the older and all benefit from having companions. Moreover, because they are of different ages the lives of all are more varied, and sharing lives in this way is itself part of one's education. As we examine the family lives of animals we may see some small likenesses to our own, but we shall see mainly differences. In one way alone we differ from all animals. No matter how long we may be away from home, we can always go back and be welcomed by our parents. This is something no animal can do, for once the youngsters have become independent, even in the best animal families, the ties between parent and youngster are broken, never to be renewed.

It is natural that we should give most of our attention to the families of warm-blooded animals, for it is in them that we see the nearest approach to a family life as we know it, but if we were to leave the others out our picture would not be complete. Nevertheless, among the cold-blooded animals, the lower animals, as we call them, anything like a family life is very rare. Such signs as there are will be of interest, if only because we do not expect to see such lowly animals as millipedes and earwigs showing mother-love. There is interest also in others of these lowly animals, especially fishes, which have novel, if still simple, ways of bringing up their families.

One thing we must always remember. No matter what means are used for bringing up a family they are successful within the needs of that particular animal. The less care the parents take, the more their young are endowed with the ability to look after themselves from the start. It could not be otherwise or life would not go on. This means that some young animals are born fully able to look after themselves. Even the most helpless can do something for themselves, if it is only to cry out in the right way to make their mother come to their aid. The secrets of how this is brought about are largely hidden from us, but that is no reason why we should not try to learn something about them.

Let us, then, start with some of the things that take place in our own gardens. Then we can wander further afield and see some of the remarkable events that take place when new lives begin.

Blackbirds

We all know the blackbird, so it is very suitable to start our story with it. It is a fairly large bird and easy to see. The cock blackbird, at least, with its jet-black feathers and its orange or yellow bill, stands out conspicuously when feeding on the lawn or in the meadow. Although a blackbird is ready enough to fly off when we go near, it does so screaming its alarm note. Even when it reaches the cover of a bush or a hedge, it still makes no attempt to hide. If need be, it still cries out with its loud alarm call, instead of slipping quietly into cover, as so many other birds do. Because of these things it is a very suitable subject for study.

The hen blackbird is as big as her spouse but less striking. She is coloured a subdued brown, with a speckled throat, and her bill is slate or horn coloured. Even so, and although she is less noisy than the cock, it is easy to keep watch on her also.

A blackbird's nest is fairly large, too, as we should expect. It may be built in a hedge, in a tree or low down in a bush. Usually it is low enough for us to be able to look into it, once we have found it, without much difficulty. The only trouble is that we may not always be able to find it readily.

For several years running, a pair of blackbirds have nested in the ivy on the trunk of an oak in the corner of my garden. I know that because it has been easy enough to watch both cock and hen collecting pieces of dried grass, and carrying them up into the ivy in their beaks. The hen collects most of the materials and does all the building, but the cock usually helps a little in finding the materials. The birds fly up to land on a branch of the oak; always they pause and look around to see if anything is watching them; and only when satisfied that they are not being watched do they fly in to where the nest is taking shape.

That is why I have not discovered the precise position of the nest, for if they see me watching, they will take a long time to enter the ivy. They hop from one branch to another, as if to put me off the scent. So, short of climbing up and possibly disturbing the nest by searching among the ivy I can do nothing about it. The ivy is so thick that no amount of peering into it, without actually pulling it aside, would tell me where the nest is hidden. The same thing happens when the young ones have hatched and the parents are feeding them. The old birds will collect worms as I dig in the garden, sometimes coming within a foot of the spade. Yet, although so unafraid then, whenever they are near the nest they do all they can not to give away its position. The result of all this is that I have never found their nest until autumn, when they have no further need of it and I can disturb the ivy without doing any harm. To do this while they are busy might cause them to desert the nest.

Blackbirds' nests are not always so well hidden. We found one this year in a fork of a small blackthorn, at the side of a green lane, only two feet up from the ground. The surprising thing is that we found this one, for even in this exposed position, if I took my eye off it for a few moments, to look at something else, I could not easily find it again. This is true for so many birds. Even if the nests are not hidden in dense foliage they are apt to blend with their surroundings.

We are fond of saying that it is blind instinct that leads the birds to hide their nests so cunningly. After a while, however, we begin to wonder if this thing we call instinct is so blind as all that. You can pass by a nest in a hedge again and again without seeing it. Yet once you have seen it, it is obvious enough to make you wonder why you failed to see it before. So, whatever be the truth of it, the way in which birds choose the sites for their nests is most effective, so much so that very few of the eggs or nestlings are lost. We do occasionally see a nest that has been robbed. Two scientists, one in Britain and one in America, have gone very carefully into this matter and both have shown that only one in every thirty of the eggs laid or of the nestlings hatched is lost. It is during the first three months after the youngsters leave the nests that the damage occurs. During that time, three out of every four die from accidents of one kind or another, either from disease, injury due to their own inexperience or from being killed by birds or beasts of prey. That is a grim side to the picture, but if there were not this weeding out the world would soon be so packed with living things of all kinds that nothing at all would survive. There would be no room for anything to live.

Let us leave that picture, however, and look a little closer at this so-called blind instinct. For this we can go back to the blackbirds, and see what takes place in that secret place in the ivy. In a cup-shaped nest of woven grass strengthened with mud and lined with more grass, the hen lays four or five eggs, bluish-green freckled with reddish-brown. As soon as the last egg is laid she begins to incubate. That is, except for short spells off the nest to ease her muscles, she sits tight on the eggs, the warmth from her body helping the growth within the shell. The cock brings her food and will sometimes take his turn at incubation, but the hen does most of it.

Each egg, like the hen's egg, with which we are more familiar, contains a rich yellow ball of yolk, surrounded by what we call the white of the egg. It is, in fact, not white until it is cooked. In the raw it is nearly transparent and acts as a protective cushion to the growing chick and the yolk on which it is nourished. When we crack a new-laid egg, all we see is yolk and white. The chick, or rather the beginnings of it, is there, but a microscope is needed to see the minute pin-point of life on the upper surface of the yolk. In a fortnight from the day the hen blackbird starts to incubate this pin-point grows in size over the surface of the yolk, until in the end of that time all that is left of the yolk is in the chick's stomach. While feeding on it, the chick has grown round it to enclose it.

The yolk is therefore a store of food provided in advance, which anticipates the young bird's needs. It is not the only way in which needs are provided for in advance. Thus, the white of the egg seems at first glance to be the same all through. In fact, there are two twisted ropes of the same transparent, jelly-like material, lying within it. One of these ropes is to one side of the spherical yolk and runs towards the narrow end of the shell. The other is on the opposite side of the yolk and runs towards the blunt end of the egg. We can see how these work if we take a disc of cardboard, make two holes near its centre, thread a string through the holes, and tie its ends to make a complete loop. With the finger of one hand through one loop of string, and a finger of the other hand through the other loop, we can spin the cardboard disc so that the string on either side of it becomes twisted. The tendency of twisted string is to untwist, and as it does so the cardboard on it spins. The force of the spin untwists the string but carries it on to twist in the opposite direction. So the disc is kept spinning first one way, then the other. The ropes in the white of the egg do something like this with the yolk, but much more gently. The effect is to keep the minute point of life, which is the growing chick, always uppermost, if the egg is rolled.

During incubation, the hen will, every now and then, rise on her feet within the nest, bend her head under her breast and, with her beak, turn each egg. Then she sits down on them again. She turns them so that no part of the egg shall be kept too warm or grow too cold. In the turning, the ropes in the white keep the growing chick uppermost, always at the point of maximum warmth. So the egg not only contains the growing chick and the food to feed it, but also a simple mechanism to keep the whole egg warm and to keep the chick itself warmest of all. It also has a hard shell to further protect the delicate chick, and this is, moreover, porous to allow air to pass through, for even at this very early stage a chick must have oxygen. One other thing may be mentioned. At the blunt end of the egg is a cavity, just inside the shell, filled with air. This contains the first gulp of air with which the young chick fills its lungs, just before it hatches.

A fortnight is a very short time for a minute speck of living protoplasm to grow into a nestling blackbird, so growth must be very rapid. There must be no mistakes. Everything must be prepared in advance and, if the growth and hatching are to succeed, everything to go according to plan. At the right time the chick must break out of the shell. To enable it to do this, there is a small horny tooth on the end of the beak, known as the egg tooth, which is shed soon after it has done its work.

At the end of the fortnight, the chick has the instinct—or, perhaps we had better say, feels an urge—to lift its head, break through into the cavity at the blunt end and gulp the air contained in it. It has now begun to use its lungs. Next, it must crack the shell. This it does by punching a circle of holes with the egg tooth and pushing the cap of shell away. If you happen to be near at the right moment you can hear it chipping at the shell. Finally it struggles out of the shell and lies helpless in the bottom of the nest. A young blackbird has been hatched.

At first the body is wet; but it soon dries, with the aid of the warmth from the mother's body. This same warmth is needed for another reason, the chick's body is naked, except for a scanty covering of down, and this alone is insufficient to keep it warm on its own. The chick's eyes are closed, and as we look down on the newly-hatched blackbird chick lying naked and blind in the bottom of the nest, it is hard to believe that one day it will be a strong, handsome bird flying about the garden. Yet, although it then looks so utterly helpless, so delicate and so fragile, it is not entirely so.

In a fortnight's time, from the moment of hatching, the limp nestling will be a fledgling, not yet able to fly, but strong enough to leave the nest. The body will have grown from barely an inch long to fully three inches. Instead of the scanty covering of down, the body will be clothed in feathers. The eyes will have opened. The voice will have grown strong. In every way and in every direction, the chick will have grown enormously.

Growth means food. Food is the raw material from which new flesh and bone are formed, and from which energy for movement can flow. A fortnight is a very short time and the young blackbird must grow rapidly. It must have food and more food. Indeed, apart from warmth, that is about the only thing it needs. And here, again, its need is anticipated, for while helpless in practically every other way it can show the greatest vigour in begging for its food.

The more helpless the young the more the parents must do for them. As soon as each nestling hatched, the hen took the fragments of shell in her beak, flew off the nest and dropped them well away from it, so that there should be no tell-tale signs to disclose the position of the nest. She keeps the nest clean in other ways, also. She removes the droppings from the nestlings. These are contained in a special envelope so that the hen can do her work cleanly. She will pick up, and either eat or carry away, anything that is likely to foul or clutter up the nest. Insects find that birds' nests are cosy places, and there are some insects that lay their eggs in the nest. When these hatch, the grubs, if not removed, would bore their way through the delicate skin of the nestlings and eventually kill them. So the hen is constantly cleaning the nest: eating the insects, or their grubs, clearing away the droppings, removing the shells, tidying the edge of the nest, so that the ends of grass do not make a litter inside it.

All this is instinctive, but it makes for a clean and tidy cradle for the growing youngsters. It is instinctive also for the hen and the cock to fetch food. They fill their beaks with worms and fly back to the nest. As soon as one of them lands on the edge the one important instinct of the nestlings comes into play. They thrust their heads upwards and open their beaks wide to receive the food, which the parent thrusts down their throats.

Let us suppose we have found a blackbird's nest, low down in a hedge. We have been very quiet so far, and as we gaze down into the nest we can just make out the nestlings huddled together at the bottom of it, for the down on their bodies is black. As they lie huddled they look more like a dark smudge at the bottom of a dark nest. Now, if we tap a twig near the nest, or lightly touch the edge of the nest, we see a transformation. The thin, scraggy neck on the plump body of each nestling is thrust upwards, with surprising vigour for such thin necks. At the same time the beak is thrown wide open so that the gaping throat is directed towards the sky. The beak at this stage in their lives is large compared with the rest of the body. It is yellow along its margins, and the throat also is a vivid yellow. When four or five nestlings gape vertically like this, it looks as if a group of vivid yellow flowers has suddenly blossomed.

Nestling blackbirds gape upwards before their eyes are open

We have nothing to offer the nestlings, yet they continue to gape for a while, straining upwards. Then, one after the other, they subside, and all we see is the dark smudge once more in the bottom of the nest. Again we tap the edge of the nest, or a twig near it, and once more the yellow throats are pushed up skywards.

Blackbirds

It is not easy to watch a blackbird in the act of feeding its nestlings, for not only is the nest, as a rule, hidden from sight, but the parents are very wary and will not feed them while we are anywhere near. They may return with their beaks full of worms, but as long as we are about, they will fly from one perch to another, in the neighbourhood of the nest, without attempting to enter it.

Very rarely we may chance upon a wild bird in the act of feeding its youngsters. Then, if we are very still, we may be lucky enough to see what goes on. Or it may be that some other accident will let us into the secret. We can take up the story, then, from something else that happened this year. A neighbour of ours was cutting back a privet hedge when he suddenly realized that he had exposed a nest of young blackbirds fully to view. The shears had cut the privet away almost level with the top of the nest. Seeing this, he withdrew and waited for the parents to come back. In spite of his precautions, it was soon clear that they were not coming back. They seemed to be aware that, with the nest and brood open for all to see, there was danger. A mouse or other beast of this kind would, under similar circumstances, carry its young ones away and make another nest for them somewhere else. Few birds can do this, so they desert them.

Our neighbour telephoned us to ask if we would take care of the nest, and before long the whole nest with its occupants was on a table in my study. The three nestlings in it still had their eyes closed, and they were clearly very hungry. Each time anyone went near them they would thrust their scraggy necks upwards and open their beaks wide. The mere vibrations of the floor-boards, as we walked towards the nest, were transmitted through the table to them, and were sufficient to make them gape.

We soaked some bread in milk and mixed with this a small amount of minced meat, and with this in a saucer prepared to act as foster-parents. The best way of feeding young birds is to use a pair of blunt tweezers, picking up a small quantity of food in these and gently thrusting it down their throats. The nestlings are incapable of holding food in their beaks, and unless it is thrust well down the throat they cannot swallow it.

We would feed each bird in turn, and as each was satisfied it would sink down into the nest and fall asleep. On the whole, we did not have to keep note of which one was fed last. The youngsters themselves told us that, because as their hunger was appeased so they gaped less vigorously. This is not invariably true, because even at this early stage, when the stubs of their feathers were only just beginning to appear, they already had different personalities. One in particular was more pushful and greedy than the others. We had to watch that one to see it did not take more than its share. It is easy to imagine that the parent bird must be in a similar position. That is, while for the most part, nestlings themselves will show by their gaping whose turn it is next, it is highly likely that in a short while the parent will need to recognize them individually.

For two days, the nestlings continued to gape straight up, with what is called the vertical gape. Then, more or less simultaneously in all three, their eyes opened, and they began to use what is called the directed gape. That is, as soon as anyone went near them they would gape, not upwards towards the sky, but directly towards that person. Vibrations were no longer necessary. The eyes were being used, and the young birds would open their beaks in the direction of any passing object.

This change from the vertical gape to the directed gape did not necessarily happen all at once. For a brief while after the eyes had opened, one or other of them might show just a little uncertainty. One of them might gape vertically, as if old habits were too strong for it, and then turn its beak towards the food. There were occasions also, when, instead of thrusting the mouth towards the food, the nestling would just push its mouth forward in whatever direction it happened at that moment to be facing.

Young animals are always attractive, and it is a pleasure to look after them merely for this reason alone. Added to this is the interest of learning more about the way they live. Not the least fascinating part of this study lies in trying to find out how much in their growing personalities is the result of instinct and how much is due to their learning. Blackbirds, as we shall see, depend very much upon their unfolding instincts.

Having never before had the job of hand-feeding young blackbirds, we wondered how often we should feed them. The question of how much to give them was easily settled; we merely pushed food down their throats until they refused any longer to open their beaks. Once their appetite was satisfied, nothing we could do would make them open the beak. As to time, they settled that for us, also. We merely had to wait until we heard them clamouring for food. When very young, they gave voice with a gentle *zee-zee-zee*, but as they became stronger their voices grew louder and they called with the well-known blackbird chirp.

There was no need to teach them when to leave the nest. With our little family it happened this way. We had made a practice of getting up early, soon after dawn, to give them their first feed of the day. One morning, about a week after we had first adopted them, I came downstairs rather later than usual. As I went towards the study door there was no doubt, from the chorus of chirping within that the young blackbirds were wanting their breakfast. I fetched their food saucer and tweezers and went in. The nest was empty.

As I stood looking at the empty nest, somewhat taken aback, the air seemed filled with insistent chirping. So I began to look round the room, on the bookshelves, on the tops of bookcases, and finally on the floor itself.

I had always supposed that when young birds left the nest for the first time they would naturally not go very far from it, and would perch on nearby twigs. But now I come to think about it, the only time I have actually seen, in the wild, a young bird leave the nest for the first time it flew straight to the ground. It was a young yellow-hammer. Its nest was about two feet up from the ground and it flew down into a tangle of grass and brambles. What is more it stayed there for at least two days.

The more I have thought about this the more likely it has seemed to me that it must be what happens with young blackbirds. I thought of the various youngsters I had seen at different times, in the gardens and in the fields, and it seemed most likely that when young blackbirds first leave the nest they must flutter to the ground. This would mean that the parents would need to do something about teaching them to fly. I shall have more to say about this in a moment. Meanwhile we must follow the further adventures of our own trio.

As I finally looked on the floor, there were two of them, each in a corner of the room, with their backs to the wall, their beaks held towards me. The third was still in the nest, lying so close to its floor that I had not seen it the first time I looked in. It was obviously sickly, and, sad to say, it died soon after despite our best attentions. The other two, on the floor, were giving full voice and stretching their beaks towards me for food. As I moved about the room, the two of them came towards me and followed me about. It was most touching; and I felt flattered that the young birds should be so devoted to me already. As I fed them I felt a great affection for these trusting youngsters. The sad awakening came later in the morning.

Now that the young blackbirds had left the nest, they were put out in the sun-room, in a large wire cage, to keep them from straying into harm's way. It so happened that, while they were in this cage, I chanced to carry past them a long strip of wood. As I turned, the end of the wood, now opposite the cage, swung towards the young blackbirds. They opened their beaks at it and twittered, just as trustingly as they had done towards me. Quite clearly, they were in no real sense attached to me and were ready to gape at anything that moved near them.

To prove this, I tried carrying all manner of objects past them. They gaped and twittered just as trustingly to each and every one of these. *When one of our cats walked up to the cage*, they did the same to him. Had the wires not been there, it would have been a short story with a sad ending for both of the blackbirds.

Fledgling blackbirds gape at any moving object

It is easy to imagine how this gaping habit helps the parent blackbirds in their task of looking after the youngsters. In the early days, just after they have left the nest, the youngsters must be fed. The parents must give all their attention to finding food. If they had, at the same time, to be continually looking to see where the youngsters were, their task would be impossible. As it is, the parents being the nearest moving objects, the young blackbirds keep near them, opening their beaks to take the food, as soon as the parents have gathered it.

This is only a brief outline of the story, of course. There is between parent and offspring a constant give and take, and much of it is instinctive. We may call it blind instinct if we like, but it is more like a key fitting a lock, opening the way to co-operation between them.

Pheasants and Ducks

SOME BIRDS build more elaborate nests than those of blackbirds, while others build hardly any nest. If we leave aside the cuckoos and a few others, we can divide birds into two kinds, those that build an elaborate nest in which helpless young must be tended for a while, and those whose chicks are almost independent from the start. The second kind usually nest on the ground, and a good example is the pheasant. I have to confess that I know much less about young pheasants than I do about blackbirds, or others that remain in the nest as nestlings for a week or two after hatching. This is because it is so much easier to study birds that cannot get away. Even so, it is possible to piece together the story of the pheasant.

Pheasants' nests are not easy to find. I believe there are people who, from long practice, can find them fairly easily, but most of us merely stumble on them by accident. Walking through bracken or the coarse grass on a common we are suddenly startled by a large bird flying away almost from under our feet. Then, if we are lucky, we see the nest, or what passes for a nest, for it is only a shallow saucer scraped in the ground with a few untidy bits of grass in it.

It so happened, several years ago, that I came upon several nests in this way in the course of one season. One of the nests was on a piece of rough ground in the outer suburbs of London, and quite near to a housing estate. This was rather a surprise to me, but the nest was probably safe there in spite of the dogs that would have been taken for exercise over this ground. Hen pheasants have their own ways of keeping dogs away from their nests, as we shall see.

This particular nest contained no eggs when I stumbled upon it. Nor did two others, and from these the hen either flew up and away high on the wing or flew low over the coarse grass. Then came the time when, walking across a common covered with thick tussocks of grass, a pheasant flew out in front of me and half-ran, half-fluttered, twisting and turning through the tussocks with a broken wing. At least, she trailed one wing as if it were broken and she gave every appearance of being injured, until she was well away from me, when she flew up and away into some nearby trees.

This is a well-known trick, used to take one's attention off the nest. Having watched it I then looked for her nest. There it was with twelve eggs in it.

Pheasants lay more eggs than a blackbird. In a blackbird's nest you usually find four eggs. Sometimes there may be five, or three, and the most ever found is nine. The pheasant's nest that has fewer than seven eggs in it is very poorly filled, and the number may often be twelve, while fifteen or twenty are not unknown. It has been said that when you find twenty or more eggs in one nest it is because two pheasants have laid their eggs in one nest. I am not sure about this. Gamekeepers often take pheasants' eggs and put them under a broody poultry hen. They will tell you that the hen pheasant will go on laying almost as long as they continue to take her eggs from her.

Last year, we had a cock pheasant and two hen pheasants in a run in the garden. In due course, one of the hen pheasants scratched a very simple nest in the earth and started to lay. We had visions of a brood of pheasant chicks growing up in the garden where we should be able to watch them every day. Unhappily, things turned out differently from this. Rats used to come into the run. At first they came in to eat the grain put down for the pheasants. They would come even in broad daylight, merely scuttling away into their holes when we went to the run, and coming out again as soon as our backs were turned. They also came at night, when we could do nothing about it, short of sitting up all night.

Almost as fast as the pheasants laid their eggs the rats would have them. I say 'pheasants' because shortly after the first hen started to lay the second hen scratched a nest in another part of the run and started in turn to lay. We gave twelve eggs to some boys who wanted to rear the chicks and in the end put five more under a broody Light Sussex hen. That made seventeen from the two pheasants, but this was far from being the total laid. How many the rats took is impossible to say. We used to find the broken shells, often at a distance from the run, and others almost certainly were carried into the holes. Altogether, although we cannot be absolutely sure of this, each pheasant must have laid a score of eggs at least.

We were unlucky with the five eggs placed under the Light Sussex hen. Two failed to hatch, and she trod on two of the three chicks that did hatch. The one survivor was like the ordinary farmyard chick but smaller, and its down was yellow mottled with black. It was soon running about and picking up food for itself, while the hen tried to help her adopted chick by scratching the earth and clucking to the chick to come and pick up the insects she had uncovered.

One chick, even if we include its foster-mother, does not make a family, so to continue the story of the pheasant family we must go back to the wild. There was another occasion when we were out walking with some friends, when a lady in our party actually trod on a pheasant sitting on her nest. It was among tussocks of grass, and to walk across the ground we had to pick our way between the tussocks and often to step over them. It was in stepping over a tussock that the accident occurred. The hen pheasant struggled free, frightened the lady nearly out of her wits, and then flew straight up and away. Pheasants are apt to sit very tight on the nest in this way, especially when the eggs are near to hatching. Unless actually touched as this hen was, they do not fly up as she did. What usually happens can be shown by a nest we came across on another occasion.

This time we were walking across a wide stretch of sandy common, covered with heather. Suddenly a hen pheasant started up at our feet and ran through the heather, sometimes over it, fluttering as if she were badly injured.

We stood, rooted to the spot by the suddenness of this display, watching the hen as she made away from us. Then she followed the usual line on such occasions, fluttered as if injured for about fifty yards or so, then flew up and away, showing quite well that she was not injured in the slightest degree. After we had watched her out of sight we looked for the nest, and found it empty.

The moment something moves, it catches our eye and holds our attention, as indeed it held ours on that occasion. It is very easy to imagine that if a dog were searching through the heather, it would follow a pheasant behaving in this odd way. The dog would pursue the bird and then, when she had drawn it away from the nest, she would fly up and out of harm's way. So we call this trick of feigning injury a distraction display. It is not deliberate on the part of the pheasant. It is the result of nervousness or over-anxiety, which, for the time being, seems to paralyse a wing or a leg, so that the bird actually appears to be injured. In any event, it distracts the attention of the dog from the nest.

I have already said that the nest, when we found it, was empty, so we were left wondering why the pheasant should have behaved in this way. The answer was presented to us about half an hour later. This time I was lucky enough actually to see the pheasant when I was about a yard from the nest. I was, in fact, searching the ground for wild flowers and, with my attention on the ground, saw from the start everything that happened. At one moment, I saw the mottled browns of the back of the pheasant as she sat in a gap between the heather. The next moment she had risen to her feet and, half-running and half-fluttering, went

Mother pheasant, feigning injury, leads the enemy away from her chicks

away to my right. At the same time half a dozen small mottled-brown bodies rose from the nest and slipped as quietly and quickly as mice into the heather, to disappear from view. As soon as they were out of sight I looked round for the hen. She was just finishing her injury-feigning and rising on the wing. She flew round in a half-circle, to land in the heather perhaps sixty or seventy yards ahead of me. She, also disappeared from view, and all we were left with was the empty nest to remind us of the episode.

This was an opportunity too good to miss. I wanted to see what the chicks would do and also what the hen would do, so I waited, standing motionless. I could hear the chicks cheeping, in the tangle of heather, and after a while, as nothing more seemed to be happening, I took a pace forward, bent down and tried to see them. A tangle of heather stems about a foot high is not an easy thing to search, especially for something having much the same colour as the stems. I gently parted the heather, the better to see. The chicks seemed to be moving about over an area of approximately a yard square, judging by the few sounds I could hear. When I moved the heather, however, they became silent and remained perfectly still. As soon as I remained still and silent, they began to cheep once again. It was a real game of hide-and-seek between us.

What the hen pheasant was doing all this time I could only guess, for she was quite out of sight. I imagined her, moving through the heather towards the chicks, listening to their calls and at the same time watching my movements. It seemed unfair to keep her in suspense, so I withdrew. When I returned later, hen and chicks were back on the nets—

or were until I drew close to it, when they repeated their performance.

We can now begin to answer a number of questions, and to pose one or two others not so easy to answer. The first thing we notice about these adventures is that, apart from the pheasants in the run in my garden, which could not get away, we have had nothing to say about the cock pheasant. He takes very little part in the family life. Yet, were he to do so we should have a different tale to tell.

A friend of mine has a handsome cock pheasant in a large aviary, and in it are a number of other fairly large birds. Not only does the pheasant rule the roost, but anyone going in to put down food, or to clean the aviary, runs the risk of receiving a vicious peck from him. If you have ever seen two cock pheasants in the fields, or in the woods, you will know that they fight savagely. Like their cousins, the barnyard cocks, they fly at each other with the neck feathers fluffed out and wings flapping, trying to strike at each other with their spurs. If only the cock pheasant stayed near the sitting hen and used either beak or spurs on the rats, there would be a different story to tell. As it is not in his nature to do this, the hen must use other means for protecting her eggs and her chicks. As we have seen, in the wild she does this, or tries to do it, by using the distraction display. It is the only defence she has.

How successful is this distraction display we can but guess because nobody has made a sufficiently close study of it for us to do otherwise. What I mean by this is that we do not know what happens to pheasant eggs in the wild, how many are destroyed, how many are left to hatch and how many young pheasants survive the hazards to grow to full maturity. We cannot judge by what happens in pheasant preserves, where the birds are protected by the keeper's gun and where food is put down so that the chicks shall have the greatest chance of survival. All we can guess is that under naturally wild conditions the number of pheasants in a given area does not vary much from year to year, yet, as we have seen, each adult hen pheasant will lay a large number of eggs each year.

On the other hand, we can speculate—which is slightly different from guessing—about certain aspects of the pheasants' family life. We can, for example, try to understand why pheasants lay so many eggs. The first thing we can be sure of is that it is a means of ensuring there shall be enough young pheasants to carry on the race. Where many eggs are laid, or many young ones born, we can always be sure that there will be heavy losses among them. This much we can take for granted since, under natural circumstances, with few exceptions, the numbers of any animal—their populations, as we say—remain more or less the same from year to year. This can mean only one thing, that there must be many offspring lost each year through natural hazards. To put it the other way round, any animal subject to a high rate of natural risks must have large families if its race is not to die out.

A hen blackbird needs to lay only four eggs at a time, because both parents tend the family and, more important, do something to guard it from enemies. The hen pheasant must take responsibility for the family alone and unaided, and the best she can do is to try to draw enemies away from the nest. As we saw with the pheasants in the garden, this is no protection against rats. It does not seem to be much protection against foxes, either, judging by the following incident. Not many years ago, somebody saw a fox disturb a sitting pheasant. She flew off and fluttered along the ground in the usual distraction display. But the fox instead of following her went to the nest and, taking each one in turn, buried the eggs nearby. No doubt it came back later to eat them. It is a habit of foxes to bury food, just as it is for a dog to bury its bone.

How often foxes steal the eggs of pheasants is not known. We have only such rare instances as this by which to judge. Their more usual food is rats and mice. Stoats, no doubt, sometimes take the eggs and the chicks; probably weasels also take them. Hedgehogs are said to steal the eggs. Hawks take the chicks occasionally, and jays and magpies may take eggs and chicks. Even if none of these habitually robs either eggs or chicks, and if all only do so occasionally, the fact that there are so many enemies means that the losses must be high. On the other hand, if nothing eats them, and there are too many pheasants, disease usually breaks out, the result of overcrowding, and thins their ranks.

If we stop and think about this, we shall soon see that all these enemies of the pheasant, the fox, stoat, weasel, rat, hawk, hedgehog, magpie and jay, will have different methods of attack. To be able to vary the defence so as to meet effectively such different situations would call for a far higher intelligence than that possessed by a hen pheasant. The best solution is, therefore, some instinctive tactics that will save the life of the hen, who can if need be return to lay and replace eggs lost, and, possibly, by this same display, do something to draw the enemy away from the eggs or chicks themselves.

There is here a nice balance. The hen pheasant is endowed with no more than a slender means to combat the enemies, but, at the same time, she has the ability to lay many eggs to offset losses. On the other hand, under ordinary conditions, the enemies take enough eggs and chicks to thin out the broods so that disease does not become rampant. This is the sort of balance we must always keep in mind, especially when we are studying the family life of animals.

Dangers to young animals are not always from enemies or disease. Sometimes they come from the parents themselves. We shall have more to say about this when we come to the four-legged animals. Meanwhile, let us look at an instance in birds. The ducks we see most commonly in parks and on ornamental lakes, as well as in the wild, are those known as mallard. The drake and duck of the mallard pair up in the autumn and keep together after the nest is built and the ducklings are hatched. The nest is of dead leaves and grass, mixed with feathers and down. It may be made in a tree, either in a hole in the tree itself or in an old crow's nest, or else on the crown of a pollarded willow. More often it is on the ground, near the water's edge, usually under a bush or other cover. The duck builds the nest, she lays the eggs, incubates them, and leads the ducklings to the water soon after they have hatched. To this extent, she is like the hen pheasant, having to shoulder the burdens of the family. Yet the drake does give her some attention, and may often be seen in the vicinity of the nest.

A mallard duck lays ten to twelve eggs, as a rule, but the number may be as low as seven and as high as sixteen. We should expect, therefore, a high rate of death among the ducklings, so we had better see what the enemies may be. The first enemy is probably the fox, which would certainly take one or other of the parents if given the chance, and doubtless will take the ducklings also. As well as the enemies on land, or in the air, ducklings on the water are a tempting sight to pike, which seize them from below.

I have little experience of seeing what happens to mallard ducklings in the wild, so I must go back to what happened in our garden. We had a pair of mallard last year, and these had a family of ducklings. The history of the parents is itself of interest. They were hatched out from eggs laid on the window-sill of a room seven storeys up from a busy London street. A large empty flower-pot stood on the sill and in it a mallard duck laid her eggs. The owner of the flat, to which the window-sill belonged, sought advice as to what should be done. He was told to leave the eggs until they hatched, then to take the ducklings out of the flower-pot or they would be led to their death on the street below.

We saw earlier that mallard sometimes nest in trees. Their nests may then be as much as forty feet up from the ground. Whether the nest is at ground level or high up in the tree the same thing happens. The eggs hatch and the ducklings enter the world, covered with down and wet from fluid in the egg. As soon as they have dried, the mother leaves the nest and calls to them. They then leave the nest and follow her to the water. If the nest is on the ground, the ducklings merely step out of it and fall to the ground, where the mother stands calling to them. One by one they tumble out, pick themselves up and with a little shake of the tail wait for the whole family to move away to the nearest water.

It might be thought that in this hazardous descent from a high tree lay the greatest source of danger. That is not so. I have talked with several other people that have watched this ceremony and none has seen a duckling hurt itself in the fall. Nevertheless, a fall from a seventh-story window into a busy street might have given a different ending, had it been allowed to take place. In any event, it was not allowed to happen and two of the ducklings eventually came to live with us.

They were lodged in a large aviary, with a bath of water in which to swim. In due course, the duck made her nest and laid her clutch of eggs. The rats used to invade this aviary, also, and although we were never able to see what took place, we know that the duck's eggs were not molested. We can only suppose that if the rats ventured near the nest both duck and drake would have driven them off.

Although we saw nothing to confirm this, I have seen rats swimming across a lake on which mallard were swimming. As soon as the mallard saw the rats they swam over to intercept them. They placed themselves across the course along which the rats were swimming, looking like surface warships waiting for submarines. Indeed, each rat imitated a submarine, for as it came near a duck it dived, swam under water and came to the surface well on the other side. If this can happen on water, and at a time when the mallard have neither nest nor ducklings, I am prepared to believe that mallard with eggs or young ones would be equally ready to attack. At least, we can say that we lost no mallard eggs to the same rats that took so many pheasant eggs.

We found that one of the biggest dangers to the ducklings was from the parents. Although tame enough before starting to nest, when the ducklings had hatched, the duck would give a low hissing sound whenever we went near the ducklings, even when taking food to them. At such times, also, she became restless and in her anxiety to protect her brood would often narrowly miss treading on them. The accidents that happened had nothing to do with these occasions, however, for we were as careful as we could be not to alarm either the parents or young ones. Moreover, because the drake was the clumsiest with the ducklings we separated him from the rest of the family, but only after several of the ducklings had been trampled to death. Of the five remaining alive when the drake was parted from them only two eventually survived.

It would be tedious to try to set forth in detail all the accidents that can happen to young ducks, but from watching the families in the wild we can be fairly sure that what happened with our mallard family must be something near to real life. First we see the duck with her brood of seven, eight or ten. Then, as we watch them during the weeks that follow we see these numbers grow less and less. It could not be otherwise unless the world were to be overrun with ducks. They are numerous enough as it is, but if all these big families survived to grow up, and have their own large families in turn, their numbers in a few years would be tremendous.

Another water-bird gives us a different picture of family

life. The moorhen, or waterhen, is a blackish-brown bird with a red shield on the front of the head and a white stripe along its flank, which lives by the sides of ponds and streams. There it can often be seen swimming on the water, with the head bobbing back and forth, quickly retreating into the vegetation at the waterside as we approach. Moorhens build a nest of dead reeds and other dead water plants, either on water among the reeds or by the water's edge. As a rule the eggs number between four and eleven, but as many as twenty-six have been counted in one nest. They are laid in April, and the parents take turns in sitting on them. When they hatch, the moorhen chicks, which are covered with a black down, remain in the nest for the first two or three days, and even after this it is about three weeks before they can feed themselves.

During this time other nests are built, to which the growing chicks can go, so that when the mother lays another clutch of eggs they are not driven away. On the contrary, the two families of chicks live on good terms, the older chicks often helping to feed the younger ones. One experienced naturalist tells of watching a half-grown moorhen looking after a younger chick, which seemed to be giving trouble. After a while, the half-grown youngster swam away, but reappeared a little later, leading back the mother, who proceeded to chastise the younger chick. It was, the naturalist said, as if the elder brother, finding the younger one more than he could manage, went to fetch his mother.

Whether this was so or not is hard to say. It is only hard to believe because we do not see behaviour of this sort, as a rule, among birds. It is, nevertheless, hardly more extra-

Half-grown young moorhen fetches parent to deal with disobedient younger brother

ordinary than the next thing we have to tell. This is to do with repairing the nest.

Sometimes the level of the water will rise and a moorhen's nest will become flooded, or will be floated away. When this happens the parents gather more materials and build it up so that its platform is clear of the water. Another naturalist tells how he watched such an event, and that he saw the parents gather dead reeds and pass them to one of the chicks, who built them into the nest, as skilfully as if it were fully-grown and used to making nests. Again, we have something that is hard to believe, merely because it is not the sort of thing we expect from young birds. In this instance, however, although only one person in this country has seen it happen, two naturalists in Germany have also seen it happen on separate occasions. It does seem, therefore, as if moorhens are a cut above most birds in family matters.

We have seen that moorhens lay many eggs at a time and usually have two broods a year. Sometimes they may have a third. The young chicks, although unable to feed themselves for three weeks, are adept very early in life at hiding, if danger threatens, either by swimming into the reeds or diving and swimming below the surface, to come up further away. Yet in spite of this and in spite of the devoted attention of the parents, very few of the numerous chicks survive until the next year. This alone emphasizes the many dangers that beset even the most devoted families in the wild.

There is another bird that lives very much the same kind of life as the moorhen. This is the coot, a black water-bird with a white bill and a white plate on the front of the head.

It lives more on the open water of lakes, but like the moorhen nests among the vegetation at the margins. The hen coot also lays numerous eggs, and the chicks take even longer before being able to look after themselves. Although they begin to look for food when they are about a month old, they are not fully independent until two months old.

The question is often asked, whether birds are able to recognize their own chicks. We can answer this so far as coots are concerned, because two naturalists spent a long time watching families of coots. To most of us, young coots all look alike, and from what these two naturalists saw, so they do to the parents until they are about a fortnight old. Coots nest fairly close together, and once the chicks begin to wander from the nest, it is not long before they find themselves in the wrong nest or going up to a fully grown bird that is not their parent. For the first two weeks, the old birds will feed any chick that happens to come near them, but, after a time, they come to recognize their own, after which a chick from another nest will be driven away, told to go home, as it were.

Matters are very different with gulls. There, as long as a chick is on the nest or within a short distance of it, the parents will feed it and defend it, and generally take all possible care of it. Should a chick wander away, however, there is every chance that its own mother, not recognizing it for her own, will kill it and eat it.

Dangers in the Air

IF A CAT has a litter of kittens and one of them strays out of the nest during her absence she does not, on her return, kill it, as the herring gulls kill their chicks. She retrieves it. That is, she picks it up in her mouth by the scruff and carries it back into the nest. Few birds do this, although ground-nesting birds will retrieve eggs that have rolled out of the nest, drawing them back with the bill. If the chick of a ground-nesting bird wanders from the nest, the best the hen can do is to call it. If the nest is off the ground and a nestling falls out there is nothing the mother can do. Under these circumstances, unless the chick can help itself that is usually the end, for the parents are powerless to help it. That does not mean that they do not try, but they are much less fitted for doing so than the four-footed beasts.

A few years ago, I had a pair of tame bullfinches. They

lived in a large aviary with a good deal of natural foliage in it. Spring came and the bullfinches built a nest. The hen laid her eggs and in due time these hatched. We are told that the best way to deal with young bullfinches in an aviary is to open the door and let the parents free. They will not fly away because the presence in it of a young family will bind them to the aviary. On the contrary, they will fly about collecting food and then fly back into the aviary to feed the nestlings.

Bullfinches have a different way of feeding their youngsters to that used by such birds as thrushes, blackbirds, robins and so many other common birds. These, as we have seen, bring the food in the beak, and when the nestlings gape, thrust it down their throats. Bullfinches half-swallow the food, and when their nestlings gape, they disgorge the food into the nestlings' throats. Another peculiarity of bullfinches is that both parents collect food, but at first the cock gives the food to the hen who then gives it to the nestlings.

For a day or so we saw our two bullfinches, both the cock and the hen, flying in and out of the aviary. They were bringing food in, feeding the nestlings, and going off for more. Then, on the afternoon of the second day, we noticed that the hen was no longer flying in and out. The cock was there but not the hen. At first we paid little attention to this, but as time passed and the hen did not appear, we began to be anxious. Perhaps she had deserted, or perhaps a hawk or a cat had killed her. The cock bullfinch also began to show slight signs of realizing that something was amiss, but he still flew in and out of the aviary.

We presumed he would be feeding the nestlings, and we

kept on hoping the hen would turn up. Other things claimed our attention, and we were not able to pay close heed to what was happening. Later, when we were able to inspect the nest, we found all four nestlings were dead. The cock was still flying in and out of the aviary, and as we were watching a strange thing happened. The cock came in once more and landed on the edge of the nest. He waited uncertainly for a while, looked first at the nestlings, then this way and that, as if looking for the hen. Then he leaned over the nest, took the neck of one of the dead nestlings in his beak and lifted its head. Having held the head up he tried to disgorge food into its beak, but, of course, the head dropped back as soon as he released his hold on the neck in order to put his beak into that of the dead nestling.

If nothing else, this incident shows the great disadvantage for birds that they must bring solid food in the beak, or in the throat, to feed the youngsters. Should the nestlings not respond there is just nothing they can do about it. The incident also stresses the great value, indeed the utter need, for the young birds to have this inborn impulse to gape upwards for food. There is one other lesson to be learned from this incident of the bullfinches. So far as I know, nothing has been written to compare with what we saw. Bullfinches are shy birds. They build their nests in places where it is difficult to see them. If, then, in the wild state, the mother should be killed, it would be very difficult, if not impossible, to see what the cock was doing. Bullfinches are often kept in captivity and it may be that this sort of thing has been seen before, but, at the least, we can say that it cannot be a common sight to see a cock bull-

Father bullfinch raises head of dying chick to try to make it feed

finch holding up the head of a dead or dying nestling in an endeavour to feed it.

It is easy enough to study the everyday actions of animals, and there are a lot of people doing it. If we do only this, however, we are apt to get the impression that these common or garden things they do represent the limits of their ability. The unusual incidents, on the other hand, those that happen rarely or which we see only by accident, are the ones that tell us more surely the limits of their abilities. If we take note of these, we have to admit that animals, like ourselves, will often rise to the occasion.

There was such an event only this year, when a fledgling sparrow came into our kitchen picking up crumbs. With two cats and a dog in the house, so tame a fledgling would have little chance of getting away with a whole skin. Realising this, I gently chivvied it out of the house and up the garden path. Hardly had I left it than it came back into the house once more. I drove it out a second time, and again it came back. It came back a third time, also, and this time when I drove it out it went carrying a fair-sized piece of bread in its beak.

I followed the young sparrow out and as it reached the same point along the garden path as before, a hen sparrow flew down to it, snatched the bread from its beak, and flew on to a nearby post. There she dropped the bread, turned abruptly towards the fledgling still on the ground, and twittered as if trying to attract its attention. She hesitated in this position for a moment, then turned and flew up into a tree, twittering all the time. Almost as soon as she had landed on the tree, the fledgling flew up, with the rather laboured and fluttering flight of a young bird not yet strong on the wing, and followed her.

There can be little doubt from the actions of the two, after they had come together in the tree, that the hen was the mother of the fledgling. Moreover, the whole course of events looked like a deliberate attempt by the hen to call her youngster away from a situation which, because of her greater experience, she regarded as dangerous.

If we have doubts as to whether this is the correct view to take, let us look more closely at what happened. First, the hen snatched the bread from the fledgling. We might take this to mean that the hen was greedy and was robbing the fledgling, although this explanation is unlikely to be correct. When she flew on to the post and dropped the bread, we could still say there was nothing unusual in it because birds often fly away with things and then drop them. Perhaps the most striking thing was the way in which she faced about, then called to the fledgling and flew up into the tree. It was all too full of purpose to be accidental.

In fact, it is by no means an uncommon sight to have a young bird in the garden so tame that it does not bother to move away when you go near it. Rather it is apt to come towards you, especially if you are having tea in the garden. Then, later, you see a fully-grown bird, presumably one of its parents, chivvying it away every time it shows signs of going near to people. In the end, the trusting bird is as wild as its parents. This kind of thing happens too often to be accidental, but you have to be on the watch to see it.

There are other ways in which the parent birds can help,

and some of these need little or no response from the young ones. An instance of this kind was brought to my notice on one occasion, when a fledgling sparrow had fallen from a nest in the eaves of a house, down through the cavity wall, and was imprisoned behind an air-brick at ground level. The owners of the house first noticed that something was amiss when they saw the parent sparrows showing especial interest in the holes in the air-brick. Then they noticed the cries of distress coming from behind the air-brick. A cat also was interested and every so often would pounce at one of the parents, which would fly up just out of reach, and no more. Whatever was happening there, it was sufficient to keep two sparrows anchored to the spot in spite of the presence of the cat.

In due course, the owner of the house managed to prise up a floorboard and take out the fledgling. Then he went into the garden and gently launched the young bird into the air. At the moment that the fledgling fluttered away from his hand, he felt a rush of air past his ear. An adult sparrow had flown past him to escort the fledgling. Together they flew across the breadth of his own garden and the one next to it. For the whole of this distance, and until they disappeared into the trees, he could see the old bird flying just under the fledgling, as if to catch it and help it along should its wings fail.

I saw a similar thing on another occasion. This time, I was standing on the roof of a building ninety feet from the ground, looking down over the parapet. Again it was a fledgling sparrow that flew by, its flight laboured and uncertain, as if at any moment its strength might give out. Suddenly a hen sparrow flew swiftly by, in the track of the fledgling, but checked its speed when it reached the fledgling and flew immediately underneath it until the young bird had reached a ledge on another roof and landed safely. The hen also landed beside it. The two stayed there for a few minutes, after which the fledgling flew off again towards a lower roof nearby. Again the hen flew after it, and again she flew just underneath the young bird until it landed safely once more.

When the fledgling first flew by me it was only a few feet below my eye-level, so that I was able to watch closely the whole proceeding. As a consequence, I have no doubt of the intention of the hen to help the fledgling should the need have arisen.

From time to time people have told of seeing this or that bird flying with one of its chicks on its back. Such stories are apt not to be believed, but they are too numerous and some of them have been told by sufficiently experienced people so that they cannot be entirely discredited. Thus, swans, partridges and grouse have been reported as flying with the young ones on their backs, and so have some ducks. The merganser, a kind of duck, is one that is said to carry its young pick-a-back, and the mallard is also said to have been seen, on rare occasions, to carry a duckling on its back down from a high nest instead of letting it fall down.

With the golden eagle it is somewhat different. The hen has been seen to take an eaglet out of the nest, fly a short way and then drop the young bird. When it had fallen about ninety feet, the hen is described as having swooped down and under it. Then she flew up level with the nest and again let her youngster fall. Once more she swooped and caught it. Apparently this was her way of teaching it to fly, for after letting it fall several times and catching it when it had dropped a hundred feet or more, she flew up with the youngster to a ledge of rock. There the two rested for five minutes before starting all over again.

There are other such stories. There was the occasion when a cygnet of the trumpeter swan was seen flying a few feet above the parent bird. Every now and then it dropped on to the parent's back, rested a while, then spread its wings and took off on another short flight. On another occasion somebody shot a young crane. It fell wounded to the ground and, after a struggle managed to become airborne, but flew weakly on account of its injuries. The parent bird flew down and under it, and as they flew off the young crane could be seen on the parent's back, still feebly fluttering its wings.

The best example of a bird carrying its young is found in the woodcock, which has been seen by a number of people under various circumstances flying with a chick held between its thighs. Usually the grip of the thighs is sufficient, but sometimes the parent will lower its head and use the bill to make a more secure hold, or it may fan its tail down and against the chick, to hold it more safely. One woodcock was watched while it carried its chicks away one by one to a new nest. As I say, this has been seen too often and by too many people to leave any doubt that it does happen. There is, however, another method said to be used by the woodcock, namely, of carrying its young pick-a-back. For some reason unknown, accounts of woodcock carrying their young on their backs have occasioned a good deal of disbelief, but it has been reported sufficiently often, and by experienced observers, that it can hardly be

Hen woodcock flies away with her chick held between her legs

any longer doubted. Having, myself, watched sparrows doing something very near to it I am inclined to believe in it.

For another sort of help I would turn now to crows. A man once told me how he shot and wounded a young crow. It fluttered to the ground, and as it half-ran, half-flew across the field, two adult crows, presumably its parents, flew down and alighted one on either side of it. Whether by accident or design, the newcomers spread their wings also, and being close beside the wounded one the effect was to support it and help it along. I asked my informant what happened, and whether the rescue was successful. His reply was that he did not know, because at the same time as the two crows flew down to the wounded youngster, he found several other crows flying above his head. These made so much noise and flapped their wings so close to his head that he deemed it better to get as far away as possible.

I once had a letter in which the writer told of seeing a bird, when it was disturbed at its nest, fly off carrying two eggs to safety. He thought it was very clever of the bird, but I had to write and tell him that the truth is otherwise. It sometimes happens a bird, in brooding its eggs, will accidentally crack one or more of them. Then, when she settles down on to the eggs to continue brooding them, white oozes out of the cracked shells on to her breast feathers. White of egg makes an extremely good stickfast, so by the next time the bird moves off the nest the white will have dried, and the eggs will be securely fastened to her feathers. So it looks as if the hen is deliberately carrying them away.

Although, all things considered, animals generally, including birds, make an extremely good job of bringing up their families, mistakes are often made. One of these has to do with nest-cleaning. A sitting bird will often be seen tidying up the nest, re-arranging the materials of which it is made, picking up fragments that have been broken off and dropping these over the edge of the nest. There is a very good purpose served in keeping the materials of the nest tidy, because young birds can easily be trapped by loose strands of hair or grass becoming entwined round their legs. Then, again, when the eggs hatch the parent or parents, according to whether one or both are brooding, will carry the egg-shells out and drop them well away from the nest. Some birds, instead of carrying the shells away, will eat them. This tidiness, which would put some humans to shame, extends also to dead leaves or any other kinds of litter that fall into the nest. Some ground-nesting birds will even tidy up paper litter thrown down around the nest. Moreover, when the young are hatched the parents will carefully remove their droppings; and they also pick up and swallow nest parasites that would otherwise harm the nestlings.

All this is most praiseworthy, provided it does not go awry, which is apt to happen if the sitting bird is badly scared, say, by somebody clumsily disturbing it. Then, in its perplexity, it may start springcleaning the nest, and in doing so may throw out or even eat the eggs.

Hedgehogs

It is sometimes said that you can find a hedgehog's nest by hearing its occupant snoring. I have never heard hedgehogs snore in their sleep although we have had several, tame and wild, living in the garden, and we are constantly passing and re-passing their nests. I have often deliberately stopped by the nests and listened for the snores, but have failed to hear them. What does happen, sometimes, is that when you go near their sleeping quarters one of them may snort. This is probably its way of showing that it objects to being disturbed. I am therefore inclined to doubt this idea that you can hear hedgehogs snore, and that it is the snores that guide you to their nests. Possibly people have mistaken the snorts for snoring.

I have purposely dwelt on this matter of snoring because people often ask: How do we set about finding a hedgehog nest? One way would be to go out and look for it by raking about among hedge-bottoms, or in the long grass. That does not get you very far. Usually one finds a nest by accident. It is not that the nests are deep in the ground, but because they are made of dry leaves, bedded down in a hollow, and are apt to pass unnoticed.

In summer, at some time from towards the end of June until the end of August, the sow, as the female hedgehog is called, retires to her nest. There her babies are born, from four to seven of them. Each baby is at first about the size of a golf ball and very nearly helpless. It is blind, and its ears are folded over, so that it is probably unable to hear. Instead of being covered with sharp spines, it merely has two patches on its back of whitish soft spines. These patches end in front at about the place where the neck joins the body.

Although we usually say newly-born hedgehogs are helpless that is not strictly true. They already have a sense of smell, and they are not so helpless that they cannot move their heads to grope for the mother when she comes in to nurse them. But that is about all they can do, and it is enough. Like most very young animals, their one demand is for food; and when they are not feeding they are sleeping. As a result, all their energy can be used in growing; and young hedgehogs grow quickly. As they grow in size, the two patches of spines begin to extend further over the back. They soon meet in the middle and join to make a continuous coat. At the same time the spines themselves begin to harden, and they turn from their original pale white, first to grey and then to a brown, marked with three rings, of which the middle one is black and the other two lighter in colour.

During the first month, while these changes are taking

place, the young hedgehog grows to about the size of a tennis ball. The head is still bare and the young animal looks very pig-like, especially about the snout. At this age, moreover, it is unable to play the familiar trick of rolling into a ball.

If there is difficulty in finding the nests, it is clearly going to be much more difficult to find out about the young ones. To do this, we must use one or other of the following methods. One method would be to keep hedgehogs in captivity, providing nesting boxes with removable lids, so as to be able to pry on their private lives. This is not easy, as hedgehogs do not readily breed in captivity, so we may have to use the second method. This is to seize the opportunity, when someone finds a nest with young ones in it, to transport them home and keep watch on them.

We let it be known in the neighbourhood that we were interested in studying hedgehogs and, sure enough, one day the desired result was achieved. It so happened that a farm labourer was working in a field with a tractor, clearing the ground, when he uncovered a nest. In it was a mother with two babies.

When a nest is disturbed in this way, the mother may either carry her babies away and make another nest for them, or she may eat them. Even if she carries them away there is a good chance that they may be found and killed by some other animal, while she is preparing the new nest. When, therefore, the mother and her small family were brought round to us to take care of them, we were only too glad of the opportunity. Since they would be well looked after and given the freedom of a large garden we had little compunction about doing so.

We built them a house of breeze blocks with a wooden roof, and filled it with straw. As the roof could be lifted off, it was possible to look at them, quietly, whenever we felt inclined to do so.

Young hedgehogs are not particularly beautiful but they are extremely attractive in their ways, and we had not had these long before the temptation to take them out occasionally to look at them, and stroke them, proved too much to be resisted. These two were probably no more than a week old when we first had them, nearer a tennis ball than a golf ball in size. They were still blind, and the flaps of the ears were folded over the opening into the ear. They were able to walk, and were quite unafraid of being handled. In fact, we can say that, taken young enough, hedgehogs are very easily tamed. That does not mean that they will not roll up when handled, but it does mean that they will not do so readily, and will unroll when their spines are stroked, from the head backwards. Once they have been stroked in this way they will remain unrolled, provided there is no sharp noise or sudden movement to startle them.

The same thing cannot be said about the mother, who had been wild from birth, and we finally set her free as soon as her babies had grown old enough not to need her. The two youngsters, now themselves grown up, are still with us in the garden, and having been able to watch them and handle them from a very early age we have learned many things about them which we could not otherwise have known.

The first thing we learned was that, very soon after we had them, even while they were so very small, the two youngsters began to develop different personalities. Although they were both treated alike, one grew more quickly than the other. It was also lighter in colour, from the moment the spines began to harden, and still is lighter now that both have grown up. It was also more shy. It was natural, therefore, that the darker youngster should have quickly become the favourite. It would not only allow itself readily to be handled, while its brother (or sister, we cannot be sure until next year) would remain quiet, but would actually crawl on to one's hand if it were held palm upwards on the ground in front of it. I am speaking now of the time before they were able to roll up.

This co-operative hedgehog came to be known as *Teasel*, after the flower-head of the plant of that name. When the two were brought out, towards the evening, *Teasel* would crawl about quite unconcernedly, testing everything around with its pig-like snout. The other one would move about, too, but only after a while. At first it remained in one spot, or, if its mother was brought out at the same time, it would try to crawl under her, although, as often as not, she was rolled up in a ball and the youngster would push against her in vain.

This led us to wonder what takes place inside the nest. A mother animal not only provides a nest for her young, and suckles them, but she must perform other duties for them, such as keeping them warm by sheltering them with her body.

A hedgehog sleeps curled up, but not fully rolled up. While in the nest, and so long as she is not disturbed, therefore, it is possible for her young ones to creep into the cradle formed by her curled body. This state of affairs lasts only while the young ones are very small, and also while their spines are soft. Once they begin to grow there is not sufficient room for even two of them, let alone the four to seven which normally form the litter, to cuddle up in this way.

If, then, the mother does not protect them with her body when they are beginning to grow, how can they be protected from raids by enemies? As we have seen, the mother, when disturbed, rolls up completely and leaves the youngsters to take their chance. But they are able to look after themselves to some extent. We found this as soon as we went to pick them up. They would start to jump on all fours, rather like a bucking horse, and would continue to do this for several seconds. Even after they had settled down again, if we were not careful how we put our hands down to them they would start again. Usually they would jump no more than an inch or so off the ground, but I have seen them jump as much as three inches into the air. If one of them jumps as your fingers are coming towards it, to take hold of it, the result can be fairly painful. The spines do not penetrate the skin to the point of drawing blood, but I have found my finger-tips irritate for quite a while afterwards. It is easy to imagine that a fox or a stoat, pushing its delicate snout into a group of young hedgehogs, might be deterred from going further with the operation. This might not be true for an old and experienced fox or stoat, but it could very well be true for a young one that had not yet learned how to deal with these living pin-cushions. It is easy to believe, therefore, that the jumping might very well be an effective defensive trick.

If I have given the impression that mother hedgehog is not a very devoted parent, the following story may help to put this right. It so happened that we received one day a call from a nearby farmhouse. Our good friend at this particular farm knew we were interested in hedgehogs and he had disturbed a family of them when working in a field. He left his tractor and came to the house to telephone.

Immediately on receiving the call, my daughter jumped on her bicycle to go and look at the nest. The farm was not far away, yet by the time she arrived there was no sign of the hedgehog family. The farmer had been busy so had no time to keep watch on them, and we can only guess what might have happened. The mother might have eaten her two babies, as I have already said, because she was scared, or she might have removed them to another place. So it occurred to me, for the first time, to wonder how the sow would carry her youngsters. We know how cats and dogs carry their babies, by the scruff; but these young hedgehogs were described to us by the farmer as being well grown, with their spines hardened. So we presumed that the mother would not carry them in her mouth.

The obvious way to find the answer was to consult such books as we had. Plenty of people have written about hedgehogs but none said anything about the way they retrieve, as the carrying of the young by the mother is called. The next step was to enquire of naturalist friends. They too, it seems, had not thought about it and none of them had seen it taking place. Carrying the enquiry further, I finally had a score of letters from people who had seen it.

Most of the letters told of the sow carrying the babies one by one, by the scruff. Others told of seeing the babies carried by the throat, by the belly, or by a hind leg. One writer described watching, at very close range, a hedgehog pick up her baby by taking its snout in her mouth. Unfortunately, none of these mentioned the approximate age of the youngsters. It may be, therefore, that the scruff is

Mother hedgehog carries her baby by its scruff

used to carry them so long as the spines have not grown forward over the neck. As a rule, any animal mother will retrieve in very much the same way on all occasions. We had, therefore, to find some explanation for those that retrieved their youngsters by a leg, or by the throat. It could well be that if the mother is in a hurry she will just seize her baby by whatever part of it is most convenient.

What interested me as much as anything else in these letters was that they all spoke of the sows being seen retrieving their families in broad daylight. In one instance, for example, the letter told of a hedgehog with her nest in the bottom of one hedge carrying each of the babies in turn across the garden to a nest in the hedge on the other side. The writer of the letter said there was no obvious reason why she should have done this. The nest had not been disturbed, so far as could be seen, unless it was by a rat.

Several other letters described the same kind of house-moving. Then there was one telling a similar story, but in this instance the mother, instead of retrieving, prodded the two youngsters forward with her snout. Their journey to the new nest in the opposite hedge took them up a flight of three low stone steps. The mother went up the steps easily enough. After all, hedgehogs climb quite well: they have even been known to climb trees. One of the youngsters also managed to climb the steps successfully. The second tried several times at the first step, but at each attempt fell over on its back. Finally, the sow, who had been waiting on the top of the steps, walked down, picked up the young one by the scruff and carried it all the way to the new nest. The mere fact that the sow not only encouraged the two youngsters to climb the steps and waited for them to do so, but also came back to help the one that had failed, suggests that she was not so unaware of the duties of a mother as might otherwise appear.

The final story in this batch of letters supports this view. This was from a gentleman who told how he had set fire to a heap of garden rubbish. The smoke from this drifted across to a hedge. In a short while he saw a hedgehog come out carrying a baby by the scruff. She carried it to another hedge, at the bottom of the garden, and then came back for another. Altogether she carried four babies away in this manner. After this, she was not seen again that day.

The garden fire smoked throughout that day, and through the night. The next day it died down and finally went out. A little later, after the smoke was all gone, the hedgehog was seen to carry her four youngsters, one by one, back to the nest she had vacated the day before.

For me, this story puts the hedgehog in a new light. We always rank the hedgehog low in the scale of four-footed beasts, and we do not give it credit for having much of a brain. This one, at least, seems to have had sense enough to know when to vacate the nest and when to bring her family back.

So far, nothing has been said of the boar, for a very good reason. Father hedgehog has no part in family affairs. The boar and the sow come together to mate, but at other times each goes its own way. The sow bears the whole responsibility for bringing up the family.

Small and Large Families

THERE are very good reasons for dealing first with the hedgehog. It is a very familiar animal; but it is something more than that. In its ways of life, as well as in the way it is made, it is very close to the first furred animals to appear on the earth millions of years ago. One sign of this is that it is not gifted with very much brain-power. Having studied it, therefore, we are in a better position to look into the family life of others with better brains than the hedgehog.

If it were possible to pick and choose, the best to take next would be either one of the man-like apes, such as the gorilla or chimpanzee, or one of the many kinds of monkeys. These come closer to ourselves in so many ways that it would be interesting to compare an ape or monkey family with our own to see what are the differences. Unhappily, very little is known about these. The next best thing, therefore, will be to take one of the most intelligent of our native quadrupeds, and for this purpose I choose the fox, mainly because I have kept foxes in my garden and watched them bring up a family of cubs.

In the woods on either side of my house we can hear the foxes barking on winter nights, a sharp *yip-yip-yip* regularly repeated. In January the vixens start to scream, a most unearthly sound breaking the still of the night. Then we know that the foxes are choosing their mates and in two to three months time litters of cubs will be born.

We can take up the story with my own foxes which, although tame, live in a large wired-in enclosure, furnished with logs, boughs and vegetation, so that they are as nearly as possible in natural surroundings. Here each fox has its separate earth, as the resting place is called, a more or less rounded chamber with an entrance on one side and an exit on the other.

Once the foxes have paired off they play together a great deal, which is doubtless their way of making love. Yet, they come together to play only at certain times of the night and day. At other times they keep apart. Certainly, they give little sign of being a devoted couple. They sleep in their separate earths, and when feeding they are distinctly selfish. This is especially true of the dog-fox. It may be different in the wild, where each can hunt for its own food, but where food is brought to them, as it is with our foxes, the completely selfish nature of the dog-fox is very marked. For example, if all the food is put in one dish, he will keep the vixen from it, throwing his hindquarters at her every time she approaches, and he does this without pausing in his eating. The result has been that we have found it necessary to scatter the food over the floor of the pen if the vixen is to get her share. Whether this, or anything like it happens in the wild is difficult to say, but it serves to bring out the very great change that takes place once the cubs are born.

We knew our vixen was going to have a litter partly from the fact that she started to dig another earth. This was merely a shallow tunnel just under the surface, which she dug entirely on her own, the dog-fox not helping her at all. So she worked alone, and as the earth began to take shape she started to strip the fur off her underside and from the insides of her legs. This she used to line the earth. In addition to providing a warm nest for the cubs, it had the effect of exposing her nipples, ready for the time when she would be suckling her cubs.

Then, one evening, the vixen did not appear when the food was put down. It was clear, however, that the dog-fox knew where she was. What was more, he behaved completely differently from usual. Instead of eating as much food as he could, and as rapidly as possible, he picked it up in his mouth and walked with it towards the nursery earth making a sound we had not heard before. It was a low gruff bark. As he uttered it, the vixen looked out from the opening into the nursery earth, whereupon the dog-fox dropped the food on the ground in front of her. The completely selfish dog-fox had now become completely unselfish.

For a whole month, the cubs remained below ground except when part of the ceiling of the nursery earth fell in. It was interesting to see that the vixen seemed to know exactly what to do. Quietly and calmly she came out of the earth, removed the fallen clods with her mouth, then calmly removed the four cubs one by one. She carried each cub in her mouth, holding it by the scruff, and then took

Father fox runs to his family with as much meat as his mouth will hold

them in turn into the dog-fox's earth, so that he had to take over the one which the vixen had previously used as sleeping quarters. He accepted the situation, making no protest and appearing readily to give up his sleeping quarters to the cubs.

For the month that the cubs remained below ground, the father continued to take food to the vixen. Apart from this he had nothing to do with the cubs, nor did he enter the earth in which they were living.

The cubs are born naked and blind, able only to move about sufficiently to find the mother's teats to take milk. She assists in this by lying in the best position for them to help themselves. The first month of life is therefore a time for feeding and growth and little more, and during this time the cubs become covered with a soft coat of smoky brown fur.

When first they ventured above ground the cubs were fat and round, with short legs, and the ears still drooping. Only later did the ears become pricked like those of their parents. Their tails were short and covered with short hair, and the cubs wagged them like any puppy. When the cubs walked their movements were awkward and they were unable to judge distances, so that in jumping even low obstacles in their path they would often become stuck halfway. Their walking was, in fact, little more than an awkward wobble.

Very quickly they grew stronger. They also learned to judge distances and heights, but very slowly. Although they could take solid food for themselves, the dog-fox still continued to bring food to them. There was a difference, however, for instead of dropping it in front of the vixen, the dog-fox would keep the food in his mouth and walk round and round outside the earth calling. The vixen would come out and take a share of the food from his mouth. Then both parents would walk about while the four cubs ran between their legs, every now and then jumping up in an effort to take food from the mouth of either father or mother. They had to work hard for their food. As often as they tried to seize it the parent would dodge and the cub would have to try again. Eventually it would be allowed to take a piece, and, after eating that, would scramble again for more.

There can be little doubt that the result of this way of feeding helps to develop the muscles of the growing cubs and improve their powers of judgment. A lazy cub would starve, but the more active cubs would get the larger share of the food. By this method of feeding the cubs were having their first lesson in how to look after themselves.

There was another way in which they were educated. This was by their play. It consisted at first of little more than scampering out of the earth, running around and bolting back into the earth at the slightest sound. Soon they began to play properly. When this happened there was such a tangle of legs and tails as the four cubs played that it was difficult to see what was taking place. By careful watching, however, as well as by taking films of the play and studying these when projected on to the screen, a distinct pattern of play could be seen.

The play of fox cubs consists largely of actions that will stand them in good stead when they come to fend for themselves. In it, one can recognize hunting movements and others that would be used in escape from enemies. Not all

Young fox-cubs taking food from the vixen

these actions come out together. For the first fortnight there are about half a dozen actions which are practised over and over again, as if to perfect them. Then comes an abrupt change. Play then consists of new tricks, with occasionally the old ones being used, as if to keep them in practice. At the end of another fortnight there is another change, and so on for about two months.

We should not have known this except that our first fox, which was the dog-fox, came to us as a cub. Living and playing on his own, we were able to study the separate actions. Then, when he grew up and was father of a litter, remembering what we had seen him do we could pick out these separate actions from the confusion of tumblings that takes place when a whole litter is playing together.

So far, then, we can see three stages in a cub's education. The first, while it is in the earth, consists of little more than feeding and sleeping, and learning how to move the limbs. Then comes the next stage, when it comes above ground and starts to play. Both the play itself and the exercise it gets in taking food from the parents' mouths are all the time teaching it the kind of movements and antics it will need when it leaves the parents and goes off to earn its own living.

The third stage is one which we could not hope to see in foxes brought up in the lap of luxury, as ours were. We can, however, see this in wild foxes, when the whole family goes out hunting. How long this lasts would be difficult to say, but while it lasts, the cubs must learn a great deal from seeing the parents hunt.

All through their infancy, therefore, the cubs are benefitting from being part of a family. They are fed at first by the mother, and later the father brings them food. They are sheltered and kept warm by the mother, who also defends them from enemies with her sharp teeth. This we know from experience, for to put your hand in the earth while even a tame vixen is there with her cubs is to make sure of having it bitten. In addition, the cubs inherit the ability to play and this comes out in a definite pattern. It is, however, much enlarged and improved upon by playing with each other and with the parents.

We find the same mixture of inherited actions and help from the parents in the matter of keeping themselves clean. At first the cubs do little more than scratch themselves when their skin itches. The rest of the cleaning is done by the vixen licking them. When the cubs come above ground, both the vixen and the dog-fox will groom them. That is, they will lick their fur to keep them clean. As time passes, the cubs gradually come to do this for themselves.

What it is that finally breaks up the family we do not know, but we can make a fairly good guess. Fox cubs are very apt to wander, but they do not just scatter. At first they are inclined to keep together in a bunch, so it is easy for the vixen to keep them near her. After a while, they grow a little more independent, although still showing a tendency to move about in pairs. Then, if he has not already departed to live alone until the next breeding season, the dog-fox leaves them. It is easy for him to do so, for the cubs cling more to the vixen, who was their sole guardian for the first month of their lives. The vixen aids the departure of the cubs, although not deliberately. What happens is that she grows more and more irritable with them, as if anxious to be rid of the burden of a growing family. She begins to snap at them if they go near her. She also takes up residence in another earth, nearby perhaps, but separate from the cubs for all that. So by a natural tendency to wander, aided by the mother's irritability, the cubs eventually leave to seek their fortunes in the wide world.

Although I have kept no other family of four-footed animals, except rabbits and guinea-pigs, I have read what other people have to say and I have kept my eyes open in wandering about the woods and fields. From all these, I have little doubt that what has been said here of foxes is true, more or less, for wild cats, stoats, weasels, martens, otters and badgers. It will also be true, no doubt, for wolves, tigers and lions and the rest of the carnivores or flesh-eating mammals.

It is a different state of affairs for the hoofed animals, all of which are herbivores except for the pigs, which will eat anything, vegetable or flesh, and are known consequently, as omnivores. The herbivores, such as cattle, sheep, deer and antelopes, show a marked difference in their family life, and in one particular more especially. That is, there is only one young at a birth, twins being very rare and triplets even more rare. Where more than one young are born to an animal normally having a single birth, the chances of all surviving are slender, so we will deal with them as if one youngster only at a time were an absolute rule.

The most striking difference, which contrasts so strongly with the helpless and hairless fox cubs, puppies and kittens, is that the young hoofed animals are almost independent from the moment they are born. That is, the newly-born calf, foal, lamb or fawn has a coat of hair, has its eyes open, its ears pricked and four strong legs. These legs may not carry it well during the first minutes after birth but within an hour the youngsters can walk fairly firmly and can run within the twenty-four hours.

A lamb can get up and walk an hour after birth

This precocious behaviour of the young hoofed animals is very necessary. Whereas a carnivore, like a fox, can go out and scour the countryside, either eating its food on the spot or bringing it home to consume it, the herbivore must eat large quantities of grass or leaves, and for this reason cannot stay in one spot but must always be moving into fresh pastures. Therefore the larger herbivores, the hoofed animals, cannot have a home in the sense that a fox has its earth and the wild cat its nest. There is another reason why the young must quickly be able to run. The herbivores are the prey of the carnivores, and must be ready to flee at the first alarm, so the young ones must be able to keep up with their parents almost from the first moment of birth.

The same is true of young giraffes, elephants and rhinoceroses, for even although these have few enemies, the youngsters of all these species are apt to be preyed upon by lions and leopards. There was a similar situation in this country years ago, in the days when there were wolves and wild cattle and deer for them to prey upon.

Because the parents must spend so much time in feeding they have less time for playing with their offspring, in the way foxes do. Cattle, horses and other hoofed animals do play, sometimes even when they are grown up, but not so frequently as foxes, dogs and cats, and not in the same way. To begin with, because they live in herds instead of families we find calves, foals and fawns playing together rather than with their parents, and their play consists mainly of running, leaping, and butting, actions which will serve later in running away from enemies, or in defending themselves if cornered.

From the large multiple families or herds we can turn to families smaller than those of foxes, smaller in the sense that the father has nothing to do with bringing up the young ones. We had one example of this in the hedgehogs. Those that follow are, however, somewhat different. For the first of these we may very well start with the long-tailed field-mouse, or wood-mouse. This is very common in woods, fields and gardens, feeding on acorns and berries, grain and almost any seeds. It also digs out bulbs and corms, so it can be very destructive in the garden. As it is nocturnal we do not often see it unless we look specially for it.

It is the size and shape of a house-mouse, but much prettier with its front and paws white. It is also much more given to standing on its hind feet and to hopping along like a kangaroo.

Wood-mice live in groups, males and females living in friendly harmony. A male and female will live together in the same nest in a most devoted fashion until the female is about to have a litter. Then she begins to be irritable and turns on her companion, the male, in a most unfriendly way. As a rule, when this happens, the male quietly departs. If he does not do so, the female will set on him with the fury of a tigress. Should he try to re-enter the nest, once he has left it, the same thing will happen. Perhaps the most surprising thing is that, in spite of the thrashings he may receive, the male makes no attempt to hit back. Sometimes he will persist in trying to re-enter the nest, for reasons that are not clear to us, and the female will savage him so that in the end he dies. This is, however, rare. As a rule he stays away, and after the youngsters have grown up and left the nest, he is able to return and live once more with his mate in peace.

Whether the male wood-mouse ever eats the youngsters, or would eat them if the female gave him the opportunity, is not known. Evidently the female is taking no risks; and this is as well, because among rodents, the males are, as a rule, somewhat unreliable parents.

Rabbits have this ever-present danger, and the does usually have their litters away from the bury, as the communal burrow is called. When the time for giving birth is drawing near, a doe rabbit goes to the middle of a field and digs a burrow, just under the surface, known as a stop. It is about two feet long, with only one entrance, and with a small chamber at the other end. This the doe lines with fur from her own breast. When her litter is born, she stops up the entrance with earth, often pulling grass over it to hide it. There she leaves her youngsters while she goes off to feed, returning at intervals to suckle them.

Whenever she returns to her litter, the doe digs the earth away to go in, but replaces it at the entrance when she leaves. As the youngsters grow and begin to move about, she leaves a hole in the entrance just big enough for them to come out and to go back in, increasing the size of the hole as they increase in girth. In the end, of course, the youngsters will scatter, never to return to the stop. It is necessary for them to be able to make these short excursions before leaving home, not only to exercise their limbs but to learn to feed. At first they take only milk, but once the eyes and ears are open they begin to chew grass. They do this at first as an exercise to the jaws, chewing the grass but not swallowing it. In this way they wean themselves gradually from milk to solid food.

This may be a convenient point to compare the families of the rabbit and the hare, animals which when adult are so very similar, yet differ so markedly in the early stages. Young rabbits are born naked and blind, and helpless except that they are able to search for the mother's nipples to suckle. So they need warmth and protection. The young hare, on the other hand, is fully clothed with fur when born, has its eyes and ears open and can soon run about once the fur has dried. The fully-grown hare does not burrow but rests in what is called a form. This is a depression in a patch of long grass which the hare has shaped to its own body. There, with the long grass arching over it, the hare can lie unseen, but ready to bolt on an instant if alarmed. The jill, when her litter is born, carries the youngsters and places each in a separate form, and, although they can run, they lie up, the mother visiting them every so often to feed them. These visits by the mother would be dangerous for the leverets if she did not do something to break her scent trail. This she does by taking a final leap to reach the form, and leaping well away from it when she departs.

It is very clear, even from these few examples, how great is the burden on the mother who brings up her family unaided. She must first find the home for her youngsters, in some instances she must make them a nest, then she must feed them and keep them clean, and, in many cases, not only do all these things but also defend them from their father. A doe rabbit, for example, instead of using a stop, may sometimes have her litter within the bury itself. If she does so, she must remain with it most of the time, leaving it only long enough to take the minimum of food, for fear the buck should find the youngsters and kill them.

In addition to this already heavy burden of duties, the mother is often called upon to defend the young from enemies. Fortunately, at such times, she is endowed with heroic courage, and whereas at other times a rabbit may be paralysed with fear when a stoat draws close to it, a doe rabbit with a litter will often fight the stoat. One such doe was seen to lash out at the stoat with her hind-legs, kicking it through the air a distance of sixteen feet. Even such a small beast as a shrew will put up a tremendous show of fury at a cat, when her babies are in danger. What is true for shrews and rabbits, is also true for all creatures even to the giants such as giraffes and elephants.

There are occasions when, in spite of this tremendous mother love, the female animal will herself destroy her own young. This may be a deplorable thing but it does happen, so we might as well try to understand why. A striking example of this occurred in our own garden. One of our cats was seen coming up the path with a field mouse in its mouth. It is, of course, natural for cats to kill small mammals, but we humans are apt to take the side of the victim, provided it is not a rat or a house mouse. At all events, my daughter went out to rescue the mouse from the cat, which dropped its prey on the path and ran away. The mouse, now free, ran swiftly up to the top of a rose bush. To leave it there could only have meant that the cat would have caught it again as soon as our backs were turned, so my daughter caught it and put it in a wooden box with some hay for a nest. An hour later, when we visited it to see if it was still alive, we found that the mouse had given birth to five youngsters. She had killed two and half-eaten a third. The remaining two were still enclosed within the birth membranes, the mother having made no attempt to free them.

We can hardly blame this wretched creature. In little more than an hour she had been caught by a cat, released, been caught by an even greater giant, placed in strange surroundings and there had given birth to a litter. This is enough to upset even so tough a being as a mouse, and mice can stand up to a great deal of punishment and live. Had she been left to have her family in peace she would have licked the babies clean of the birth membranes, and these she would have eaten. That would be a natural impulse, the result of which is to keep the nest tidy and clean, just as birds have the impulse to carry the shells from the nest and drop them some distance away after the chicks have been hatched. In addition, she would have licked her babies clean of the birth fluids.

It seems clear enough what had happened to the captured mouse. The turmoil of events had utterly confused her simple mind. The impulse to lick her babies had started to work and had been perverted to one of chewing instead. Just as it is so very easy for a slight disturbance or annoyance to turn us in a second from light-hearted enjoyment to intense anger, so the mouse's mother-love had been changed to cannibalism. We cannot blame her.

When animals eat their young, we can always be sure that it is due to some disturbance or to great danger. If we disturb the nest, frighten the mother badly, or do anything to upset the even flow of events, we upset the pattern unfolding in her brain. She cannot reason things out, and all her actions are guided by an instinct, the working of which must not be upset if it is to carry her successfully to the end. Even under natural conditions such things as overcrowding can have the same effect. When animals grow too numerous and are crowded within a given territory they become quarrelsome. One result of this is that fewer babies are born, and even those that are born will be more liable to be killed by the father or eaten by the mother. In this way a natural check will be kept on too great an increase in population.

There must be some such explanation as this for mother animals killing their own offspring, for mother-love is very strong. How strong it is we have already seen, but it is brought out even more strongly in certain unusual incidents. For example, many a bitch, having no puppies of her own, has gone into the fields, brought back young rabbits and has tried to nurse them as if they were her own babies. Unusual adoptions of this kind are not uncommon. Two scientists once tested the mother-love of a rat. They took her babies out of the nest and put them on the ground a few inches from it. Out came mother rat and picked up her babies, one by one, by the scruff, and carried them back into the nest. Before she had finished, the scientists had added young rats from other nests. The indefatigable mother retrieved them all, and she also retrieved young rabbits, even very young kittens, placed near her nest. In the end, she had her nest filled with over a hundred young rats, rabbits and kittens. It was, perhaps, a little unfair to play such a trick on a devoted mother, even if she was only a rat, but it does at least show how powerful is mother-love, and how strong is the willingness to adopt babies other than her own.

Babies in Living Cradles

There are some animals that could not possibly have followed the example of the rat that piled its nest with all kinds of youngsters. Only those that retrieve with the mouth could have done this, or anything like it, and not all four-footed beasts retrieve in this way. For many, the youngsters use some form of pick-a-back riding, if we can also use that term for those that cling to the front as well as the back. Although we are dealing here mainly with animals living in this country, we have to go abroad for examples of pick-a-back riding.

We can conveniently start with the baboons. These live among the rocks in the southern part of Africa, but these rocks are merely places where they rest and shelter. They must go elsewhere to feed. In the early morning they set out as a troop to forage. The troop includes old and young males, old and young females, and small youngsters of varying ages. Their food is green vegetation and fruit, insects and almost any small animals they can catch.

The troop consists of several family parties, and although all share equally in the life of the troop, there are some members which hold a higher rank, or a more commanding position, within the troop. This is very much what we should find if several human families were living together, and it is helpful to imagine the baboons behaving towards each other very much as men, women and children would if several families always spent their days together. There would be special friendships, bickerings, favouritisms and quarrelling; there would be some wanting to take the lead, to lord it over the rest, and some who resented this. On the whole, however, there would be a general harmony, with one person to whom everyone else would look for advice and leadership.

The leader of a troop of baboons is an old male who has won, and keeps, his position by fighting. Although he lords it over the rest of the troop, he also makes himself responsible for their safety. But the troop does not rely wholly on his vigilance. It is one of the advantages of moving about in bands that there are many pairs of eyes and ears watchful for danger. The enemies of baboons are more especially the leopards, that lie in wait, well-hidden and ready to pounce with alarming speed, so the baboons must also be ready to retreat without hesitation and at a fair speed.

In the search for food, also, the members of the troop are mutually helpful: there are more hands to turn over stones looking for insects and scorpions, and more eyes to look for likely feeding places. We can, then, imagine the troop moving across country, turning over the stones as they go, stopping at some promising vegetation, with eyes busy both looking for food and watchful for enemies. Even while thus busily occupied the baboons must be ready to dash away at the first alarm. Obviously, the females cannot leave their babies among the rocks when they go out foraging. That would be too dangerous. They must take them with them. They cannot carry them in the mouth, as a cat or a rat would, and there is only one way to solve this problem, by having the youngster clinging to the mother. When very young the baby baboon clings to the mother's underside, but as it grows older it will sit on her back, jockey fashion, as she rushes away on all fours, holding the fur of her shoulders or neck if she has to gallop speedily.

Monkeys, near relatives of the baboons, spend most of their time in the trees, also in troops. They travel along the branches, leaping from branch to branch, and in these journeys hands and feet are needed, and their youngsters must also cling tightly to mother. How they cling seems to be unimportant. Sometimes the baby monkey has its arms round mother's neck and the legs wrapped round her waist. More often it will travel spread-eagled across her tummy, gripping her sides with both hands and feet. Sometimes baby will travel clinging head downwards to mother. When the baby is very young, the mother usually manages to spare one hand to cradle it, but it must be ready to cling on its own for a moment when she needs both hands for climbing.

A form of pick-a-back riding is used by a few other animals. The giant anteater of South America carries her baby clinging to her enormous bushy tail, with its head resting on her back. The tamandua, a near relative of the

The sloth provides a living cradle for her youngster

anteater, of South and Central America, lives all its time in the trees, feeding on the ants inhabiting rotten tree-trunks or those that build their nests on the trunks. It has a long tail which it can wrap round branches for added support. The young tamandua rides on the mother's stout tail, and wraps its own tail around hers in order to cling securely.

Sloths, of South and Central America, also live all the time in the trees. Their youngsters travel like the baby monkeys, clinging to the mother's underside. Since sloths often hang upside down, suspended by their hook-like claws, the underside of the mother is often uppermost, forming a comfortable cradle for the baby.

The pangolins live in Africa and southern Asia. Their bodies, as well as their long stout tails, are covered with overlapping scales so that pangolins are often described as looking like animated fir-cones. Some of them live, like the tamandua, all their lives in trees, feeding on ants. Their youngsters travel, like the young tamandua, with their tails wrapped around the mother's tail. Even the pangolins that live wholly on the ground carry their youngsters in this same way.

The cradle formed in which the sloth carries its baby when hanging by all fours from a branch may be very comfortable, but it cannot be more so than the natural cradle provided by the flying lemur for its baby. The flying lemur is one of those odd animals that does not seem to be closely related to anything else we know. It is not really a lemur although it was at one time thought to be, because of its sharp-pointed face and large eyes. It lives in the Philippines, where it is known as the colugo or caguan, as well as in Indo-China and Malaya. Its home is in the trees, and although it does not fly in the true sense, it is better equipped for gliding than any other living animal. About the size of a cat, it has a web of skin running on each side of the body, from the chin to the tips of the fingers, then to the tips of the toes and thence to the tip of the tail. When airborne, gliding from one tree to another, the flying lemur looks more like a living umbrella. When at rest it clings by its sharp claws, upside-down on the underside of a branch. The baby flying lemur clings to the underside of its mother's body when she is gliding. When the mother is at rest, the baby rests in the soft and comfortable hammock formed by her body and its parachute.

There are a number of other four-footed beasts that glide. These include flying squirrels, which, like the common or garden squirrels, have their litters in a nest in the trees. Unlike the flying lemur, they do not carry their youngsters about with them, except when it is necessary to take them to a new nest, and then they carry them in the mouth. The only four-footed beasts that truly fly are the bats. These, as we know, fly out, usually at dusk, to feed, and while resting, as they mostly do by day, hang upside-down by their feet. The mother bat has one baby a year, twins being exceptional. It is born naked and blind, and clings to the mother's fur during the first few weeks of its life. During that time also it is carried about by the mother while she is out on her feeding flights. When it has grown too big for her to carry it, she hangs it up at the roost before setting out.

Another animal that carries its young pick-a-back is the common or Virginian opossum of North America. This is about the size of a cat but looks more like a large rat. It is

Baby opossums cling to mother's back to be carried about

the animal that has given us the well-known phrase 'playing 'possum'. When its safety is threatened its hair becomes dishevelled and it lies, perfectly still, to all appearances dead. Then, when the danger is past, it jumps up and runs away. One of the early drawings of the opossum is in the first of four large volumes published by Albertus Seba, a Dutch naturalist. This shows the mother opossum with her tail arched over her back. Five young ones are shown clinging to her back, and for further support each has its tail coiled round that of the mother. This is how the Virginian opossum has been portrayed for the last two hundred years, and it is only seven years or so ago that an American zoologist showed it to be wrong.

Perhaps we can give the truth about the opossum first and then pass to the fable. It is a pouch-bearer, which means that the female has a fold of skin on her abdomen into which the youngsters crawl at birth. There they are suckled, and they remain in the pouch until old enough to crawl freely. Even when they are out of the pouch they use the mother for transport, the whole family, which may number as many as fourteen, climbing on to her back. They grip her fur with their toes and they wrap their tails around any part of her that the tail touches, but they do not hold her tail in the way we are always shown.

When a litter of opossums is first born, the whole lot will rest comfortably in a teaspoon. Each youngster looks little more than a shapeless mass of flesh. The body is smooth without sign of hair. The head shows little sign of a face. There is a short tail and four limbs, but the chief thing we notice about it is the large gaping mouth. The front legs are fairly long and bear the beginnings of fingers, but the hind-legs are small and weak. The young opossum, when first born, is only just starting life. It is, in fact, at the stage in life when most other four-footed beasts are still within the mother's body and not due to see day for some time to come. The remarkable thing is that although it is without eyes or ears, has only weak legs, and altogether is not yet fully formed, it can find its way to the pouch clinging to the mother's fur. Once there, it seizes one of the teats in its mouth and simply hangs on, feeding and doing little else except grow.

In sixty-seven days the young opossum grows to the size of a young rat. Its body is then covered with fur, its limbs are strongly formed, its eyes and ears have opened, and it is ready to leave the pouch. But it does not curl its tail round that of the mother, so we had better see how the mistake arose. In the late seventeenth century an artist, Maria Sibylla Merian, went to live in Dutch Guiana, where there is another kind of opossum, very like the Virginian opossum. Maria had painted a picture of brightly-coloured insects and had a space left in the bottom right-hand corner. She filled this with a drawing of the opossum, with her tail stretched out behind and with six young ones on her back each with its tail curved round that of the mother. It was a piece of artistic licence and, until five years ago, everybody had copied the idea if not the actual drawing.

The Virginian opossum has a number of relatives in South America, in addition to that drawn by Maria Merian. All are pouch-bearers, but whereas in some the pouch is a complete bag with a fairly small opening, in others it consists of little more than folds of skin enclosing the teats. The same is true of some of the pouch-bearers of Australia.

In some, such as the kangaroo, the pouch is fully formed, a roomy bag with a narrow opening, but in others it consists of little better than flaps of skin.

Australia is always looked upon as the real home of the pouch-bearers, or marsupials, as they are more usually called. There are, however, quite a number of them in South America, but there they are mainly small, the cat-sized opossums being the largest of them. In addition, we know very much less about the South American marsupials than those in Australia, where live the kangaroos and wallabies, the koala, native cat, wombat, bandicoots and a number of others less familiar by name. Of them all, the kangaroos are the best-known, and they have been known for the longest time.

Although we speak of them all as pouch-bearers we have to remember that only the females carry a pouch. The males have nothing to do with the youngsters. Just before a kangaroo is born, the mother takes up a half-sitting position, usually reclining with her back against some sort of support. Her long strong tail rests on the ground directed between the hind-legs. The mother then licks a path through her fur, from the opening of the birth-canal to the opening of the pouch.

As in the Virginian opossum, the young are very small. Even in the large red and grey kangaroos, standing five feet high, the newly-born youngster is little more than an inch long; and there is only one at a birth. This makes its way through the mother's fur, along the path she has licked, crawling with a strong over-arm stroke of its fore-legs, which are much longer than the hind-legs. Thus, naked, blind and with the rest of the body only half-formed, it makes its way unaided into the pouch, takes hold of a teat in its mouth, and there stays until it is grown sufficiently to run about on its own.

Kangaroos have been known to us for about two hundred years, yet it is only fifty years ago that we finally knew for certain that a young kangaroo did, in fact, find its way unaided into the pouch. Several people had suggested this was so, even as far back as 150 years ago, but it seemed so unlikely that this tiny, almost shapeless, mass of flesh could make the journey alone, that few would believe them. One of the things that misled most people was seeing the kangaroo, just about the time that the young was born, putting her front paws and often her head also into the pouch. So they argued that either she picked the newly-born kangaroo up with her fore-paws and placed it inside the pouch on to a teat, or she did so with her mouth. We now know the explanation, that just before the birth, she cleans the inside of the pouch with her tongue, and while doing so holds the mouth of the pouch open with her paws.

Although the baby kangaroo is independent enough in some ways, this does not mean that the mother takes no part in its early life. She anticipates its coming by grooming the inside of the pouch and also by smoothing a path through her fur for the youngster about to be born. Later, when it is able to leave the pouch for excursions into the world around, it uses the pouch as a resting place and also as a retreat. Should the young kangaroo be out taking exercise and something alarms it, it will run back to the mother and leap head first into the pouch, quickly turn round inside and then peep out through the opening. The mother may help its entry by holding open the mouth of the pouch for it to leap in. If the alarm is so sudden that the young one cannot reach the pouch, the mother will make a particular call, and upon hearing this the youngster will crouch perfectly still in the grass while the mother dashes off for safety, and to draw off the enemy, returning later to allow the youngster into the pouch.

It might be thought that the pouch-bearing method has much to be said for it, but there is one great disadvantage. When the young kangaroo is growing up, it occupies so much room that the pouch is stretched enormously. This must hinder the mother's movements. The koala, or Australian Teddy Bear, another pouch-bearer, has a method which is an improvement on that used by the kangaroo. It has several young at a birth, and as these begin to grow they leave the pouch and ride on the mother's back, in the perfect pick-a-back style.

A last method of carrying the young should be mentioned: that used by elephants. The elephant family forms part of a herd, which consists of females of all ages, together with young ones ranging from newly-born to about three years old. The adult males are not with the herd all the time. They have their separate territories, and they join the herd as it passes through that territory. The leader of the herd is the oldest female, and she keeps all the others in order, if necessary thrashing them with her trunk if they break the laws of the herd.

The young elephant is born with eyes open and the body covered with hair. It has, indeed, more hair then than it will have when it is fully grown. It is also able to run about almost from the moment of birth. There is, therefore, no

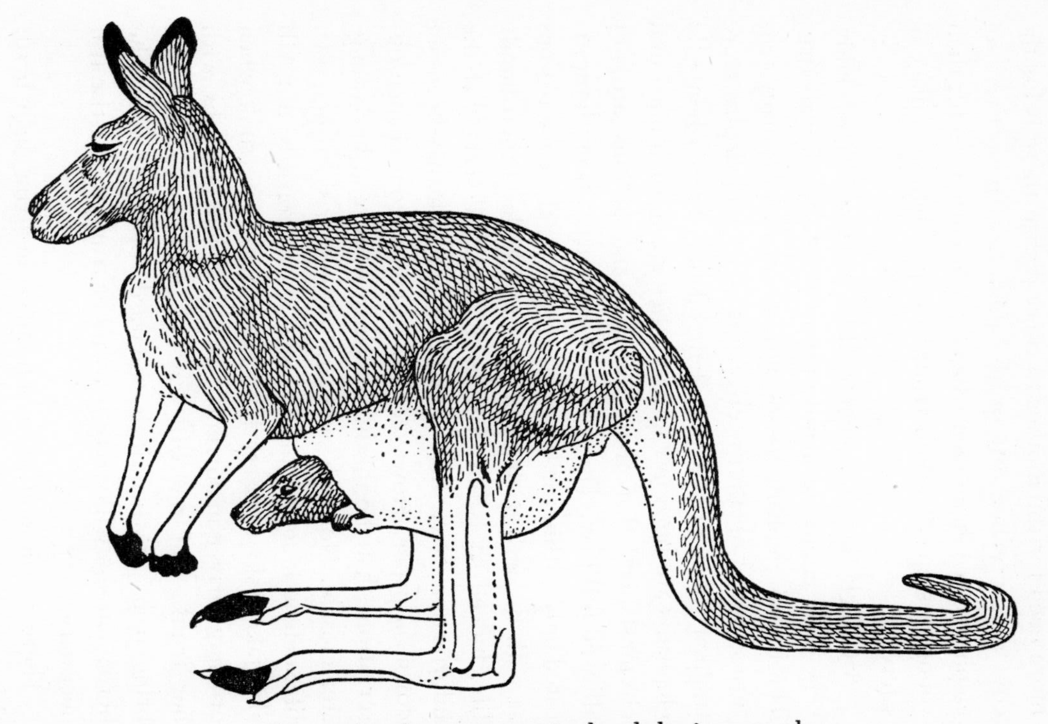

The mother kangaroo carries her baby in a pouch

more need for the mother to carry it than there is for the cow to carry her calf or the deer her fawn. Even so, elephants have been seen when in tight corners to lift their youngsters up with their trunks and put them in a place of safety.

Although they are such well-known animals we know very little about the family life of elephants, for all that. The Indian elephant has been domesticated for many centuries, but to obtain the elephants used, wild elephants are trapped when already past their infancy. Even when wild elephants are born in captivity, they are in such unnatural circumstances that their instincts and actions are not allowed full play. The African elephant has been domesticated only within the last century, and for the same reasons as with the Indian elephant we know little of their family life. Indeed, it is only within the last few years that the information given here about the herd life has been set down on paper. However, we do know from chance observations that the mother elephant does tend her youngster closely. Not only will she, often at risk to her own life, defend it against marauding lions or leopards, but will also take risks to carry it to safety with her trunk when crossing a river in torrent. She will caress her baby with her trunk, and she will use the trunk to catch it and bring it back when it is wayward, or strays from the herd; and she will strike it with her trunk to chastise it if necessary.

There is yet one more advantage in living in a herd. When the baby elephant is born, and also while it is still young, other females in the herd, especially those without young ones, will show much interest in the newcomer.

The result of this is that the mother with an infant elephant usually has a companion keeping close beside her, who will assist in its care and protection. She is, in fact, a sort of mother's help.

Crocodiles and Frogs as Nursemaids

A FRIEND of mine has a curious pet, but an attractive one. It is a spectacled caiman, from South Africa, one of the crocodile tribe. This caiman is only a young one, barely more than a foot long, so it can be comfortably housed in a large glass aquarium. My friend likes to show off his pet to visitors, although it is not particularly well-tempered with human beings. To do this he takes the caiman out of its aquarium, but before doing so he takes the precaution of putting on a pair of stout leather gloves, for protection against the caiman's snapping jaws, although these jaws are little more than two inches long.

Not all crocodiles, alligators and caimans are large, but even a caiman four feet long, which is about the smallest that a fully-grown caiman would measure, would be more than four times as powerful as the young caiman in the aquarium, of which I have spoken. The largest crocodiles, on the other hand, are twenty feet or more long, even as much as thirty feet. In dealing with these, we have to reckon with heavy and powerful animals, nearly twice the length of an ordinary living room, and having jaws two feet or more long and armed with stout teeth.

Most female crocodiles do no more than lay their eggs in the sand and leave them there to hatch. When the young ones break out of their shells, however, they call and the mother hearing this digs at the sand and helps them to get to the surface. Moreover, when the eggs are about to hatch the female crocodile appears to be irritable, if not actually bad-tempered. So, keeping my friend's small caiman in mind, it is easy to imagine that an irritable or bad-tempered crocodile, twelve, twenty or more feet long, with large snapping jaws, is something which most of us would give a wide berth. Perhaps this is why we know so little about their habits.

At least, we know that most members of the crocodile tribe dig a pit in the ground in which to lay their eggs, and that the female then remains on duty beside the nest until the young are hatched. Although she may not deliberately protect the eggs, because she is short-tempered with anything that comes near the effect is much the same. To what extent she protects the young ones after they are hatched is uncertain, because nobody has taken the risk of trying to find out. Certainly, newly-hatched crocodiles can move about on their own, and can feed themselves. They are also, like the young caiman, not entirely without the ability to defend themselves, so that not a great deal of parental care is needed. On the other hand, at least one naturalist has told how, when trying to catch a young crocodile in the water at the margin of a river, he found himself being attacked by a fully-grown crocodile. Whether she was the mother or not it is impossible to say, but this grown crocodile fairly leapt at him out of the water as he stood on a tree trunk leaning low over the river. It is not usual for crocodiles to behave like this towards human beings. Rather they try to get out of their way, so this one may have been an enraged mother.

In contrast to the usual crocodile habit of merely digging a pit in the sand, the long-snouted crocodile of West Africa and the North American alligator both make nests of vegetable matter. The female scrapes it together into a mound and in the centre of it she lays her eggs. Although she does not incubate her eggs but leaves this to the heat from the decaying vegetation, she does not forsake the nest but visits it at frequent intervals. Then, one day, she hears the young caimans that have hatched out making hiccough-like calls. She scratches away the vegetable matter from the top of the nest, and when all her family have successfully climbed out, she makes her way to the water, her youngsters following. They are able to keep up with her from the start. They can also feed themselves from the first few hours of life, and, presumably, they can defend themselves, for they are as vicious and ready to bite as their mother.

This amount of parental care is about the most we find in any reptiles. Female turtles, we know, visit sandy beaches to lay their eggs. They dig a pit in the sand, lay their eggs in it, fill the pit with sand again, smoothing it over with their flippers to hide its whereabouts, then go back into the sea. The young turtles, on hatching out, have to find their own way to the surface. Then they instinctively make for the water, fairly skipping and hopping down the beach and plunging into the surf. Tortoises also lay their eggs in the earth and show no more concern for their offspring than do the turtles. Of the lizards and snakes, some lay eggs and are said to be oviparous. Others are said to be ovoviviparous, which merely means that the eggs remain within the mother's body until they are about to hatch, which they do either just before or at the time they reach the outside world.

Some snakes do slightly better than this. The female python coils her body around her eggs, completely hiding them under the coils, and remains so until the eggs hatch. Other snakes lay their eggs in heaps of rotting vegetation, and such places, and some of these give a certain amount of attention to the young, but usually it is about as much as that seen in crocodiles and alligators. On the whole, however, we are singularly ignorant about the early stages of snakes. This we can, perhaps, best illustrate by a story about our common adder.

In 1577, a certain William Harrison wrote that he once saw an adder that lay, as he thought, sleeping on a molehill, and that out of its mouth came eleven young adders each about a foot long. These played about in front of the mother until they noticed him standing by, whereupon they disappeared again into the mother's mouth. He tells how he then killed the adder and found each of the young ones inside her shrouded in a distinct cell or pannicle, like a soft white jelly.

This story has been repeated many times, and other

people have since claimed to have seen the same thing happen. I have had letters from people who claim to have seen it happen just as William Harrison described it. And, indeed, one often hears people say that young adders when alarmed take refuge in the mother's stomach.

Do mother vipers swallow their young to protect them?

The more one learns of the ways of animals, the more one learns not to be surprised at anything, but so far as this story is concerned the experts tell us there is no truth in it. It is, however, of interest to try to find what it was that William Harrison may have seen. First, we know that the adder is ovoviviparous. Therefore, if William Harrison happened to come along as the young ones were being born he might have seen some on the ground already moving about. Then when he killed the mother and opened her up he could have found other young ones still in the egg membranes inside the mother. That could account for part of the story.

We still have to account for those he saw disappear into the mother's mouth. Those who have studied adders tell us that the young adders, even when first born would have difficulty in passing down the throat of the mother, because, they claim, she cannot easily swallow even a small lizard. On the other hand, they tell us, young adders when alarmed will dive under the mother's body out of sight. At the same time as they do this, she lowers her head, so it could easily be that to William Harrison, and to the others who have claimed to see this, it looked as if the youngsters were diving into the mother's mouth, when in fact they were diving underneath her as her head came down.

If the legend of the adder does nothing more, it draws attention to the fact that young adders do remain with the mother for a certain amount of time after they are born, and that she gives them some measure of protection. In this there is a close resemblance to what we have seen in the alligators and crocodiles, and, as we have seen, it is about the nearest to a family life found in reptiles.

Reptiles do no worse than the frogs that breed in the pond in my garden. Every year, in February or early March, according to the weather, the frogs come in from the surrounding gardens. Once they have started in the direction of the pond, they lose little time in reaching it. I watched one, on one occasion, cover the last thirty feet in a series of hops without pausing until it had plunged into the water. When they have all assembled we hear them croaking for a night or two, then they are gone. One or two latecomers may still be there, but the main body is nowhere to be seen. Instead the water is thick with masses of jelly.

Some time after the frogs have departed the tadpoles break out of the jelly-covered eggs. They swim about for weeks, at first fish-like but later growing legs. Finally, with their tails growing smaller and smaller, they leave the water as froglets. The story is too familiar to need telling in fuller detail. The main point in setting it forth here is to show how little attention the common frogs of this country pay to their offspring. The same is true for most of the frogs and toads throughout the world, but there are some exceptions. There is, for example, a South American frog that makes a nest. The male digs mud or sand from the bottom of the river or pond, choosing shallow water for this work, so that the circular wall he builds stands up above the level of the surface. The female lays her eggs in the water enclosed within the wall and there the tadpoles remain until a flood washes away the wall and sets them free.

Also living in South America are some poison-frogs. They are small and black but with brilliantly coloured patches of yellow, green and red on the body. Their skin contains a poison with which certain tribes of South American Indians tip their arrows. The female poison-frogs lay their eggs on land, and having done so depart, but the males stay behind near the eggs. This is a strange thing to do, for there seems to be no question of their protecting the eggs or taking care of them. It all seems very odd until we see the tadpoles hatch, wriggle towards the head of the male squatting nearby, and fasten themselves to his lips. When they are all clinging to him, he goes to a pool, enters the water and drops his passengers, who then lead the life normal for a tadpole.

Although we are so used to the idea of the eggs of frogs and toads being laid in the water, there is nothing very remarkable about frogs or toads that lay their eggs on land. It is, of course, unusual, but there is a sufficient number of frogs and toads in various parts of the world that do this. The best example is seen in the Stephens Island frog. This lives on a tiny island of that name in Cook Strait, New Zealand. The cap of this island is strewn with large boulders, and in among these lives the frog, with no stream or pond, or even a tiny trickle of water, except when it rains. The eggs are laid on this waterless land and when they hatch, it is not tadpoles that come out but perfectly-formed froglets. The whole of the tadpole stage is passed within the egg.

Then, again, there are some tree frogs in Africa and also in south-east Asia which go to the edge of the water to breed but do not enter it. As the female lays her eggs she paddles the mass of jelly with her hind-feet, and the froth so formed hardens to a crust, with the eggs inside it. This queer nest is, however, only temporary. Within a very short time the jelly inside the crust liquefies, slowly dissolves away the outer crust and the tadpoles fall into the water below. There seems to be no point in making this nest, and the best we can say of it is that after hearing this odd story we need not be surprised at anything frogs or toads may do.

In the forests of Chile is a frog known as Darwin's frog. The male, as is so often the case, croaks continuously during the breeding season and has vocal sacs on the sides of the head to increase the sounds he makes. This is not unusual. The male of the edible frog that has been introduced into this country from the Continent also has such vocal sacs. They are balloon-like when blown out, and stand out prominently on the side of the head, but the only opening to them is inside the mouth. The male of the Darwin's frog picks up the eggs with his mouth as soon as they are laid, and from the mouth they go into his vocal sacs. How he does this is not known. We only know that the eggs are found in his vocal sacs, that the tadpoles live in them and that the froglets eventually escape from them through the father's mouth to the outside world.

In West Africa there are a number of different kinds of toads that lay their eggs on land. In some of these the females brood their eggs. That is, they sit over them until they hatch, to release fully-formed froglets. In others, no eggs are laid, the froglets being born fully formed.

It seems as though South America has more unusual frogs than most parts of the world, and returning there we find a female of a species of tree frog which, instead of sitting on the eggs has the eggs sitting on her. The eggs are large and each is contained in a tough transparent skin. We do not know how the eggs get on to the females back. It is sufficient that they do, that they stick there, and that she carries them about until they hatch. A near relative of this frog goes one better. She has the eggs on her back, and a horseshoe-shaped fold of skin comes to lie over them and protect them. There is a third kind of tree frog in South America, the female of which has a pouch of skin on her back with a very small opening into it near the hind-end of the back. How the eggs were made to enter this was a mystery until last year, when it was seen that at pairing the male pushed the eggs into the pouch with his hind-feet. There are several species that do this. In some the eggs hatch and, when they are half-grown, the tadpoles escape into the water to finish the early part of their lives in the usual way. In other species, the tadpoles remain in the pouch until they have changed into froglets.

We have left two of the best-known toads until last. The first of these is the midwife toad of south-west Europe. The name is not very appropriate since it is the male that bears the burden of the family. Midwife toads pair on land, the eggs being laid in strings which become thrown into loops as they are laid. The male pushes his hind-legs through these loops and, having done this, retires under a stone or into a hole in the ground. He carries the eggs about with him for three weeks. Should the weather be dry, he comes out at night, goes to the nearest pond and dips the eggs into the water to moisten them. All this time the tadpoles are growing inside the jelly-like strings. Like the tadpoles of our common frog in the early stages of their lives, those of the midwife toad breathe through feathery gills on the sides of the head. When the tadpoles have reached the stage of losing their external gills, the male midwife toad

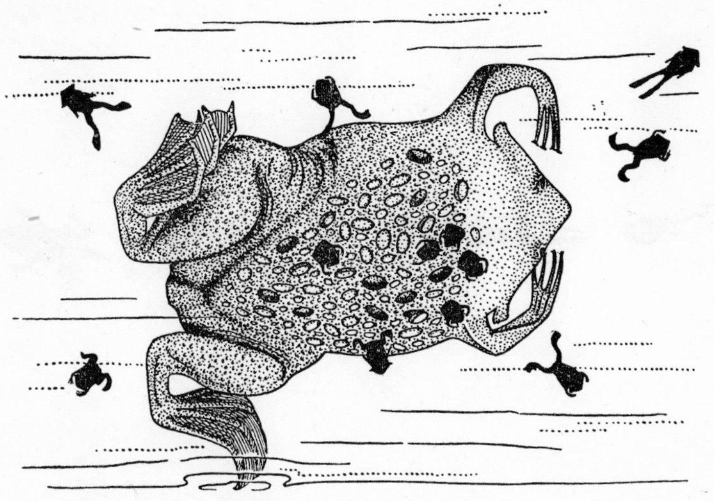

The surinam toad carries her family in pockets on her back

goes to a suitable pond, where the tadpoles can make their escape and there finish the rest of their tadpole lives.

The Surinam toad, again of South America, lives wholly in water. Its body is unusually flattened, and when pairing the eggs are passed up on to the mother's back, to which they stick. This is not the end of the story. Gradually the eggs sink into the mother's skin, so that each comes to lie in its own pit, completely out of sight. What is more, the skin forms a lid over each pit. Fully protected and out of sight, the eggs develops into tadpoles and the tadpoles into froglets. Then comes the day when first one lid is pushed up and out pops a froglet. This is soon followed by another and another, until all the froglets have left their strange homes on the mother's back.

Devoted Fish Fathers

Some years ago, we were living for a while on the outskirts of a small country town. A shallow stream wound its way round the town. In some places it was perhaps ten feet across and several feet deep, while in other places it was little more than a trickle between the stones, except after very heavy rains. All along its course, the bed of the stream was stony, with anything from small pebbles to rocks a foot or more across littering the sandy bed. One day, soon after our arrival, we were wandering along the banks of this stream when we saw a flash as something darted under one of the middle-sized stones. The water was not deep at this point so we stepped into it and lifted the stone, in the hope of seeing what this dark shadow was that had disappeared so quickly under it.

As we lifted the stone a fish darted out. This was what

we had expected, and it was not long before we had driven it into the shallow edge of the water, where it could only wriggle. It was a greenish fish mottled with black and about four inches long. There was little that was beautiful about it, and the large head made it look ungainly, even ugly. It is this large head which gives it its name of bullhead, but it is far better known as the Miller's Thumb.

We had taken care to put the stone back as we found it, and, after taking a look at the fish nearly stranded at the water's edge, we withdrew to the bank to watch what would happen. Once we were out of the way the fish flapped and wriggled its way back into sufficient water to be able to swim. It darted first this way, then that, but eventually we saw it go back under the same stone from which we had dislodged it.

The cavity under the stone was the home of the Miller's Thumb, and doubtless all the way along the stream were other stones, each with one of these fishes living hermit-like, permanently in residence. You can sometimes see them out by day, but it is mainly at night that they leave their strongholds to forage. This does not mean that a Miller's Thumb does nothing by day but sleep. It may rest, but it is ever watchful, and if anything comes near the entrance to its home it rushes out to the attack. If it is another fish, it will drive it away by charging furiously at it. On the other hand, if it is an insect larva or a snail it will eat it.

We turned over a number of stones during the next few weeks. Under most of them we found insect larvae, small snails, freshwater shrimps, bloodworms, and the like. These are the things the Miller's Thumb feeds on. Every now and then we would dislodge one of the fishes as we moved a stone. We tried to remember which stones covered the home of a bullhead, and whenever we went along by the stream we would keep a lookout for the fishes themselves. As a rule we saw little of them, unless we went to the trouble of lifting the stones. Then, on a day in March, we noticed something different. Quite by chance we saw sand being pushed out from under one of the stones. Or perhaps I should say we thought we saw this. Then, as we watched, it became clear that digging operations were going on.

At that time of the year the male bullhead becomes restless. He attacks any intruder near his home with greater ferocity, and at the same time he enlarges the cavity under his stone. Then, one day, a fish swims near and he rushes out, as usual, to attack, but this time the intruder does not swim away. She lies still and submits to the blows rained upon her, for she is a female bullhead. Spawning time is at hand and she must find a home for her family. Because she has not fled at his attack, and because she submits meekly to his fury, the male bullhead knows her for what she is and allows her to enter his home.

Once inside, the female turns upside-down and presses her underside against the stone forming the ceiling of the chamber. She stays in this position for a whole day, from twenty to thirty hours, before laying her eggs, which stick to the ceiling. All this time the male bullhead has paid little attention to the female. He does not court her, nor does he assist in any way with the egg-laying. Because his home has been enlarged there is room for the two of them without getting in each other's way. As soon as the female leaves, however, his real task begins. He fertilizes the eggs by pouring his milt over them, and then for a whole month he tends them.

During this time he continues to keep at bay anything venturing near his home, but he also ensures that there is a constant flow of water over the eggs. This he does by fanning with his breast fins. We know that this steady stream of water is essential to the eggs because of what happens if the male bullhead is taken away. Should he be killed or, as sometimes happens, should he forsake the nest, the eggs become covered with a fungus and do not hatch. That constant stream of water is vital to the welfare of the eggs, and without the devotion of the father the eggs would not hatch. Once they do hatch, however, his responsibilities end. The young fishes can look after themselves.

The devotion of the male bullhead is in strong contrast to the behaviour of many other fishes, especially those living in the sea, which merely lay their eggs and leave them to their fate. A parental care, such as is shown by the male bullhead, is more common among freshwater fishes and those living on the shore between tidemarks. One of the best known is, of course, the common three-spined stickleback. Everybody knows that it builds a nest, but it is not always easy to see this happening. One way is to keep sticklebacks in a large aquarium, but this is not always successful. Another way is to combine patience with luck, patience to watch after having the luck to catch the nest-building in progress.

We had the luck this year to be told by a farmer friend that the sticklebacks were building in the stream that ran through his farm. The water was shallow and clear, and by lying flat on the bridge and looking down into the water several nests could be seen, well spaced from each other. The nests were already built when we heard about them. Each was made of the stems of water plants and of roots and other pieces of vegetation, the whole cemented together by glue from the kidneys of the male stickleback, for it is the male only that makes the nest.

Even if we had known in time, it is doubtful if we should have learned much of the way in which the stickleback does his building. As soon as he has added more material to the nest he throws himself against the parts already made, as if testing the strength of it. All this commotion is, however, part of a plan, for after having laid the foundations the sides begin to grow up and meet above. Finally, the nest takes the form of a barrel-shaped mass of vegetable matter with an opening to one side, resting on the bed of the stream. It looks flimsy enough, as if any sudden movement of the water would sweep it away. The stickleback has guarded against this, for as soon as he had completed the platform forming the foundation, he goes to the bottom of the stream, thrusts his nose into the fine sand and brings up a mouthful. This he disgorges over the foundation. He repeats this action until enough sand has been added to weight the nest and keep it steady in one position.

Even when a nest appears to our eyes to be completed, the stickleback continues to work on it. He is continually going into the nest, turning round and round inside, and adding more glue from his kidneys, until the inner wall has been securely cemented. The building of the nest is, in more than one sense, a labour of love, which extends over a period of several days. Then, when it is at last fully completed, the stickleback is ready to look for a mate.

During the building operations, to which he has given so much attention, the male stickleback has not been unaware of what has been going on around him. If any other male stickleback has ventured too near, he has charged, with his red throat shining brilliantly and his three spines standing straight up. He continues to do this, even after the nest is finished, and then one day he rushes at another stickleback swimming towards his nest. Instead of turning tail and fleeing before his determined charge, this one gently tilts herself, with her head up, so that her swollen body is presented to his view. She is a female seeking for somewhere to lay her eggs. By her swollen body the male recognizes this and his whole manner changes. Instead of attacking her, he shows her his red throat. It is a form of betrothal. The two have exchanged signals and each is aware of the other's intentions.

What happens after this is all laid down in the book of rules packed away somewhere within the body of each stickleback. We can call it instinct if we like, but this does not mean that we know better how it works. Certainly, the sticklebacks themselves work more or less to rules, as all sticklebacks have been doing for a long way back in time. Another thing of which we can be sure is that the little set piece that follows is a sort of sign-language.

Having exchanged their preliminary signals, the male then swims away from the female on a zig-zag course towards his nest. She follows him in the same way, so that we see what appears to be a simple dance. Arrived at the entrance to the nest, the male comes to rest in the water with his head directed towards the opening. Then he moves rapidly and jerkily backwards and forwards, almost as if nodding towards the nest. The female enters it, leaving her tail still protruding, whereupon the male butts her flank with his snout, and she starts to lay her eggs.

Once the female has laid, that is the end of her family responsibilities. Like the bullhead, the male stickleback now goes in and fertilizes the eggs.

During the time that the young sticklebacks are taking shape within the eggs, the male guards the nest. He drives away any other sticklebacks that may come near, rushing at them with his three spines erect and his fins spread, in a truly ferocious manner. He will also try to drive off any other intruder. The centre of his world for the time being is the nest and its contents, but he does more than guard them. The nest is, in fact, a blind tunnel through which a current of water can pass. Oxygen is necessary for the safe development of the growing youngsters within the eggs, and this is ensured by the male stationing himself head-on to the entrance and fanning the water in with his breast fins. Every now and then, to make sure each is getting its full supply of oxygen, he shakes up the eggs with his snout. He may even drag them out and tuck them in again, carefully rearranging them.

When the young sticklebacks hatch out, he pulls down the upper part of the nest, leaving only the platform formed by the foundation. There the youngsters remain, still fanned by the father's fins, for their need of oxygen is even greater now. Within them is stirring the impulse to wander, and some are ready to leave home before the others.

Male stickleback dances to attract the female and lead her to the nest to lay her eggs

Should they do so, the male catches them in his mouth and returns them to the nursery. As more and more of them show signs of swimming strongly, however, his vigilance begins to relax. He contents himself with merely swimming round the nursery, keeping guard, while the youngsters try out their fins. In the end, he swims away, leaving them to look after themselves.

It would be idle to pretend that we saw all this by lying on a wooden bridge across a stream and gazing down into the water. The full story, a brief version of which I have given here, has been worked out by keeping sticklebacks in aquaria, so that they can readily be kept under observation all the time and everything they do noted. Nevertheless, once you know the full story, it is possible to watch the fishes in the stream and see enough to piece the story together. It is even more difficult in the sea, and the opportunities for keeping marine fishes in aquaria are fewer than with freshwater fishes. So, although there are more marine fishes, we do not know as much about their family affairs as we do in the case of the stickleback. However, we might as well look briefly at what is known.

I suppose everyone, sooner or later, likes to go poking about on the sea-shore, especially where there are rocks and seaweed. Very largely, this is because what we find there is so different from what we find inland. We do not have to search long among the rock-pools left by the tide before we see something flash rapidly across the bottom of the pool and disappear. It reminds us of the way our old friend the Miller's Thumb would disappear. If our curiosity is sufficient to make a closer search, we shall find, in due course, that the dark streak that vanished is a small fish that has now come to rest at the edge of the pool or else has disappeared under the seaweed. In either case, it is coloured so like the bottom of the pool that it tends to escape observation. Once we have found it, however, its likeness to the Miller's Thumb is unmistakable. It is, in fact, another bullhead, a close relative of the one living in the freshwater streams.

On the other hand, the fish may be a small wrasse, a goby or a blenny, but the story is much the same. Most of these make nests, either of seaweed or of shells or small pebbles, and usually it is the male that tends the eggs, although on rare occasions the female will help. Another marine fish that uses these methods is the gunnel or butterfish. The female lays her eggs within the gaping shell that once held the body of an oyster, or else in a hole in the rock. Then, either the male or the female, nobody is sure which it is, wraps its long, somewhat eel-shaped body around the shell or over the hole in the rock.

The butterfish is well enough known, although it lives more in the shallow water just beyond the edge of the tide. Yet little is really known for certain about it. We know the eggs are protected by one or other parent wrapping its ten-inch long body round the egg-mass, but we do not know how the eggs are aerated. Possibly it is by the same method as that used by the lumpsucker. This is a good example of a fish that lays its eggs on the shore between tide marks. Somewhat squat, the lumpsucker may be ten inches or so long, and it has a sucker on its breast by which it can cling to rocks. The female lays her eggs in a crevice in the rocks. There may be a hundred thousand in a single egg-mass, coloured dark brown, pink, red or yellow. Once the eggs are laid the female goes her way, leaving the male to look after them. He is so attached to the eggs that he goes without food rather than neglect them, which is just as well, for the eggs face numerous dangers. Under even the most favourable circumstances the male lumpsucker is kept busy enough. For one thing, the eggs must be aerated all the time. This he does by fanning them with his fins or blowing water on them with his mouth, and there is a strong likelihood that the butterfish must do something of the sort, but nobody has yet caught it in the act of doing so. Every now and then the male lumpsucker thrusts his head into the egg-mass. This ensures that the eggs at the centre of the mass get their fair share of oxygen. Another danger to the eggs comes from the starfish, crabs, winkles and other small animals that crawl over or come to rest on them. They may not actually eat or injure the eggs but they may suffocate them. So father is kept busy picking off the unwelcome visitors. Father lumpsucker suffers from a great disadvantage. Unlike so many other fishes that brood their eggs, the lumpsucker cannot coil his stout body round them to protect them.

There is often a sad end to this story of parental devotion, for twice a day the tide goes out leaving the beach uncovered. So, when the tide is high, larger fishes and crabs are apt to find the eggs and devour them, despite the best efforts of the lumpsucker to drive them off. And when the tide goes out down come the gulls, as well as rooks, crows and starlings, seeking what they may find in the way of food; and they often find the lumpsucker eggs. Rats also invade the shore and take their share. Despite the numerous dangers, however, nothing will drive the lump-

Male lumpsucker removing periwinkle which might crawl over the eggs which he is guarding in the crevice beside him

sucker from his precious charges. If you find one guarding the eggs and pick him up, the moment he is put down he goes back immediately on guard. As you may well guess, when gulls, crows and rats are foraging, they are as likely to feast first on the devoted father and after that take the eggs. So although many lumpsucker eggs are laid, the number that survives is not very great.

Most of the fishes living in the sea take no care of their eggs. They are laid and left to their fate. Large numbers are eaten by other fishes, but because they are laid in such vast numbers enough survive to carry on the race. In most of them a single female may lay up to half-a-million eggs, and in some of them it may be five, ten or over twenty million. It is mainly in fishes that spawn between tide-marks or in rivers that we find some attempt being made to protect the eggs, either by making a nest or by using some other method.

So far we have looked at fishes that build nests or nurseries, and we have made a brief mention of those, by far the more common, that merely lay large numbers of eggs to offset losses. A very few use a method, better known to us through the kangaroo, of a brood-pouch. One of these is the well-known sea-horse that looks something like a living chessman. Here, again, it is the male that takes on the family responsibilities. A sea-horse swims upright, and on the belly of the male is a small opening leading into a pouch. In the breeding season the female sea-horse lays her eggs in that pouch, and the male takes on the duties of nursemaid until the young have hatched and left the pouch. This method has several advantages. The eggs are aerated by receiving oxygen from blood-vessels lining the pouch.

There is, therefore, no need for the father to spend time fanning the eggs with his fins or blowing water over them with his mouth. He also has no need to fight enemies, he need only seek safety in flight, carrying the eggs with him, whereas others that show a parental care must try to keep a territory around the nest free of intruders.

Perhaps the best way of illustrating what keeping a territory means is to recount an incident which I watched in one of the tanks at the London Zoo several years ago. In this story, also, we shall see another way in which fishes guard their young. What I saw there must be a common sight not only in the Zoo's Aquarium, but also in the tanks of those who keep tropical fish as a hobby. In the tank at the Zoo were some black-banded cichlids. These are fishes belonging to a family spread all over Africa, most of South America, and up through Central America to Texas. There are two species, also, in India and Ceylon.

This particular tank was 3 feet square and 4½ feet deep, and the cichlids shared it with several other kinds of tropical freshwater fishes. A pair of the cichlids had established a territory within the tank. That is, within an invisible box, so to speak, although smaller than the other fishes, the cichlids held complete sway. If any other fish approached it one of the cichlids would swim towards it and drive the intruder away. Although there was no actual box bounding this territory, the reference to an 'invisible box' serves to illustrate one of the remarkable things about this incident, that the walls of the territory were as clearly defined as if the cichlids were in a glass box and the rest of the fishes were outside. In chasing away an intruder, a cichlid would dash to the boundary of its territory and stop short just at that boundary just as if it had bumped its nose against a wall.

It was easy to see that this pair of cichlids was about to breed because the colours of the bodies were so bright, this being especially true of the male. He it was that did most of the attacking. Before spawning, the female spent a fair amount of time digging pits in the sand on the floor of the territory with her mouth. Sometimes the male would join in this. Then they chose a flat stone on which the female would lay her eggs. This they set about cleaning scrupulously with their mouths.

When the eggs were laid and fertilized, both parents took part in their care. One of them stationed itself over the eggs which were now sticking to the surface of the stone, fanning them with fins and tail. This not only aerated them but also kept on the move any spores of fungi that might settle and make the eggs mouldy, as would have happened to the eggs of the bullhead had they not been fanned. Every few minutes there would be a change-over, with the other parent taking charge of the fanning. In addition to keeping the eggs aerated and free from fungi, the cichlids would every so often take one of the eggs and eat it. This would be one that had failed to be fertilized and was now addled. Left there such eggs would have gone black and spoilt the good eggs.

A few days after they were laid, the eggs were removed from the stone to one of the pits, each parent taking part, carrying a few at a time. As one carried, the other stood guard. Some days later the eggs were transferred from this pit to another. This is probably a way of keeping them clean, putting them in a fresh basket, so to speak.

When the fry hatched the parents were even more watchful. For most of the time the young cichlids kept together, but if one of them happened to stray one or other of the parents would swim over to it, take it in its mouth and put it back among the others.

As time passed, the young cichlids grew bigger, and as they did so the parents showed less and less interest in them. Finally, the family broke up.

There are certain fishes known as mouth-breeders. The black-banded cichlids are not true mouth-breeders, but having studied their actions we are in a better position to understand those of the mouth-breeders. There are a number of cichlid fishes that merit this name. They begin in much the same way as did the pair of black-banded cichlids, but instead of laying the eggs on a spawning site, the female mouth-breeder snaps up each egg as soon as she has laid it and the male has fertilized it. Finally, she may have 100 to 400 eggs in her mouth. You can tell which females are carrying eggs. The floor of the mouth is pressed down by them so that the throat appears swollen. Quite obviously, while carrying them she cannot eat.

The particular cichlid I have in mind comes from Natal, South Africa, but there are plenty of others that behave like it. In this one the female is silver-grey in colour, but if she is disturbed or alarmed while carrying her eggs, dark bands appear on her body. Later, when the young ones are hatched, these changes in colour as well as the things the mother does, serve as signals to the young ones.

At first such signals are unnecessary, even when the young are newly-hatched. Soon, however, they begin to escape from her mouth. First one gets out and she chases

Cichlid parents with their newly-hatched young

it and snaps it up again. Then others try, and in a short while she tires of retrieving them and the whole brood leaves the mouth. They still keep together, however, and follow the mother as she swims around. So long as she swims quietly, the fry move about in a group, or school, as it is called, feeding as they go. Suddenly there is danger. The mother tilts her body so that the head is lower than the tail, and swims backwards. As she does this, the young cichlids, instinctively recognizing this as a danger signal, swarm around her mouth, some even hanging on to her jaws. If the danger increases she continues to swim backwards and, opening her mouth, allows the young ones to swarm in to safety.

In case of great danger, the mother may not stop to take up her babies but may sail straight in to the attack. As she does this her whole body turns nearly black. This constitutes a danger signal, but with a different meaning. This time, on seeing the signal the young cichlids scatter and dive to the bottom. There they remain until the mother has driven off the intruder, when she swims down and snaps them up one after another. The first time this happens, she may keep them in her mouth for an hour or so afterwards. As time goes on she keeps them there for no more than five to ten minutes. It is as if she is learning not to be anxious. After four or five days she does not even trouble to snap them up. Quite naturally, the young are becoming more independent and the mother is taking less care of them. Soon she will be able to begin feeding again in earnest, and it is not long after this that the family breaks up altogether, the youngsters going their way and the parents separating until the next breeding season.

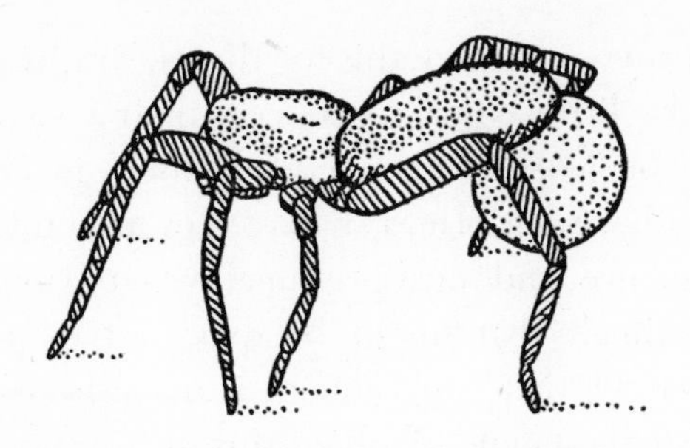

Mostly about Spiders

SPIDERS are ruthless killers, not only of their prey, but often of their own kind. This may be why few are prepared to have anything more to do with them than to watch them at a distance. Certainly their appearance is not very attractive, although, oddly enough, most people hesitate before killing them, and some would not do so under any circumstances. Yet even spiders can have their gentler moments especially for their youngsters. This is not to say that there is much in the way of family life among them. Rather the reverse, for most spiders lay their eggs and leave it to Mother Nature to act as nurse-maid, which means that they have to take their chance against being eaten or otherwise destroyed. They solve the problem of the next generation by laying a fairly large number of eggs, so that a reasonable number of young spiders shall survive the risks to reach full size. The most they do is to lay their eggs in a protective wrapping of silk, known as a cocoon, and this presumably gives a fair measure of protection. Exactly how is difficult to say because no-body has looked very closely into the matter. What we do know, and anyone can see this for themselves, is that many spiders make little effort to conceal their cocoons. They hang them on grass stems, or place them in crevices in bark, and other such places, where they are quite obvious to our naked eye, and must presumably be obvious to birds or other animals that might be expected to prey upon them. It may be that concealment is not especially necessary and that the tangle of silken threads forming the wall of the cocoon is difficult to pierce, thus ensuring the safety of the eggs. At any rate, most spiders show no care for the eggs or for the young which hatch from them. There are, however, some exceptions to this, and among them are the wolf spiders.

Spiders are very numerous. One naturalist has calculated that in places there may be as many as two millions spread over an acre of land. So it seems that whatever methods they use for bringing up their offspring they must be successful. If we have any doubt about this we can easily prove it to our own satisfaction. We have only to go into a wood or other such place where there are plenty of dead leaves covering the ground on a warm day in late spring. I would choose this sort of place because the spiders show up well against the leaves. Visit such a place and you will almost certainly see hundreds of wolf spiders running about over the dead leaves. In fact, their numbers are almost unbelievable.

These particular spiders are called wolf spiders because instead of spinning webs and waiting for their victims to fly in, they hunt their victims on foot. With their long legs they can move very quickly and, like wolves, they run their prey down.

The female wolf spider lays her eggs in a silken cocoon which she carries about fastened to her own body. In summer these females can often be seen in the grass, or better still, on bare earth, running along with the round white bag of silk, almost as big as their own bodies. You would think it would be a burden she would be glad to lose, yet should the white bag fall off she immediately turns and will not go on until she has fastened it again in position. In fact, from the way she behaves you would think that bag means everything to her.

In the ordinary course of events the bag does not fall off, and we only know how great is the female spider's devotion to it because several people have experimented with it to find out. One scientist caught a female wolf spider and carefully detached the cocoon from her body with a pair of fine tweezers. Then he let her go. Instead of running away, as we might have expected her to do after being handled in this way, she started to run around searching for her silken bag, which the scientist had hidden. Instead, he put a pellet of blotting paper, of about the same size and shape as the cocoon, on the ground. This she found and fastened to the hind end of her body. Then she departed, satisfied that everything was now in order. It did not matter whether the substitute offered to her was a pellet of blotting paper or of cotton wool or a cork ball about the same size. This is, however, not the end of the story, and the rest of it puts a different light on this seeming devotion of the mother spider.

By continuing the experiments the following things were found. If a spider has been carrying a dummy cocoon for only a short while and a real cocoon is put down near her, she will drop the dummy and pick up the real article. She will do this even if the cocoon is one made by a female of another species. It was also seen that some females deprived of cocoons would not pick up anything, dummy or real, especially if some hours had elapsed before they were given the opportunity to do so. It began to look as if the spiders could not only recognize the real from the false, but also that memory was playing a part. More experiments were clearly necessary to test this. As a result of these, it was found that the mother spider's devotion depended upon what was taking place inside her body. If her eggs were not yet ready to be laid she would more readily accept a substitute for the cocoon, and would do so up to forty hours after having been robbed of it. Should she be ready to lay, or if she had already laid her eggs, she made less strenuous efforts to find her cocoon, if robbed of it, and after about two hours took no notice if it was given back to her. Another thing that was found was that if the cocoon had been newly-made, the spider 'remembered' its loss for longer than when she had been carrying it about for some time.

The cocoon is carried, if not interfered with, for five weeks, at the end of which the eggs in it hatch and the young spiders come out and run about on their own. If given a dummy she would carry it about for the same length of time as she would have done had it contained eggs that were going to hatch. So, after all, it is not the youngsters she is concerned with but the cocoon. In the end, so long as there are no scientists about to play tricks on her, it amounts to the same thing: she carries the cocoon about until the eggs are hatched. Moreover, she does not need to know they have hatched, the state of her ovaries dictates the time when she shall drop the cocoon.

Although the young spiders are able to run about as soon as they hatch they keep close to the mother. Should anything disturb them they run to her, climb on to her back and cluster there while she runs under cover for safety.

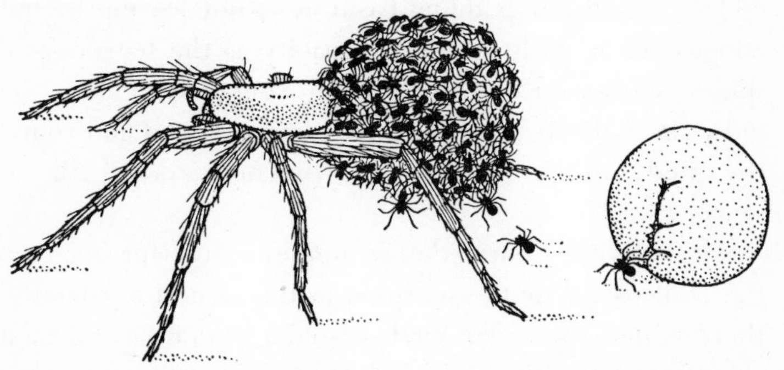

Female wolf-spider carries her family pick-a-back

They also cluster on her back to rest. So the family continues together for about a week until the youngsters are big enough to look after themselves entirely. Like the scorpions, which are closely related to them, and which also carry their young pick-a-back during the early days of life, the mother spider is used merely as a means of transport. She does not feed her offspring and, being cold-blooded, they have little need for warmth, so that here we have family life at a very simple level.

The position is slightly better with centipedes, which are also related to spiders. Here the female not only makes a nest for her eggs but guards it until the eggs have hatched and the youngsters can look after themselves. The nest is made of mud and looks rather like a small pudding basin turned upside down. It has a hole in the top to let air in, because even eggs must breathe, but the hole is not large enough for a full-grown centipede to enter. This is just as well because the male centipede will eat the eggs if given the opportunity. As it is, to reach the eggs he would need to pull the nest to pieces. The female prevents this, lying coiled around her pudding basin nest, not leaving it, but clinging to it with the same tenacity as the female wolf spider shows for her cocoon. If you disturb her, the most she will do, as a rule, is to crawl round and round the mud hillock which forms the nest, rather like a sentry.

Although the centipede has gone one step further than the wolf spider or the scorpion in the care of her family, there is one particular kind of spider which has taken it even further and has more of a family life than any other spider. To begin with, both male and female live together in a single web, which alone is unusual, because with most kinds of spiders the two lead very solitary lives. They come together during courtship and mating, and even then the male must make a hasty retreat after mating or stand the risk of being eaten by the female. In this particular spider of which I speak, not only do the male and female share the web in complete harmony, but the young spiders also live with their parents, even sharing their food. Such a state of affairs is, however, as we have said, most unusual. By far the majority of spiders pay little attention to their offspring. Nevertheless, there is a kind of family life, if we may so call it, among some of the young spiders themselves. For example, when the eggs of the garden spider hatch the spiderlings keep together, and combine to spin a web which forms a sort of nursery. In this they remain for a while before dispersing.

We had a very good opportunity last year to watch how young spiders leave home, so to speak. We did not actually see the young spiders leave the cocoon, but we must have seen them soon after, certainly within an hour. By then the young spiders had spun a small web on a creeper in the conservatory at about four feet from the ground. It was a sheet of silk, quite unlike the web of the garden spider with which we are familiar. It was about six inches in diameter, and on it between one and two hundred young spiders were bunched together in a tight ball, measuring about an inch in diameter, forming a golden blob on the dark-green of the leaves of the creeper. We probably should not have noticed them then but for the way they behaved. If we went near the creeper, and especially if we did anything to vibrate it, the young spiders would begin immediately to move outwards in an orderly manner. It was very like the way members of a drill squad scatter on being dismissed. In due course, the whole brood would be evenly spread over the six-inch web. Then, when things had settled down once more, they would begin to trek inwards again until the tightly-packed mass had been re-formed.

The young spiders remained in this place for two or three days, then they migrated in a body to a point about a foot higher up on the foliage of the creeper. The following day they split into two groups, which parted, one going an inch or two in one direction and the other an inch or two in another. In a very short while, however, the two groups came together again to form the one solid mass

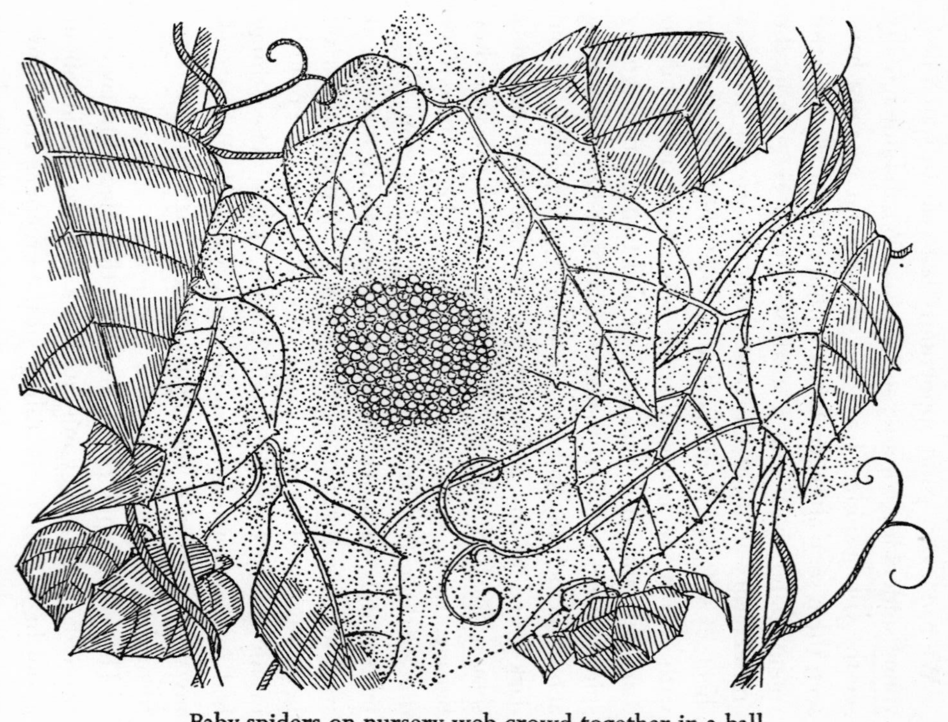

Baby spiders on nursery web crowd together in a ball

once more. A day later they had split again into two groups and this time their ways really parted. Both groups moved upwards all the time towards the roof of the conservatory, one going to the left, the other to the right. Whenever they moved they laid down a very fine track of silk, and whenever they came to rest they spun a fine sheet of silk. When they had, finally, all gone their several ways the course of their journey was marked as clearly as on a map, by the silken tracks they laid down as they went.

On the creeper could still be seen the original platform of silken web with the path of silk going up from it, showing where the two groups had diverged and later came together again. Higher up were the two broad ribbons of silk, forming a V about a foot or so in height, showing where the two groups of spiders had finally parted company. The left-hand group had soon dispersed altogether, and their further wanderings were marked by a number of irregular single strands of silk, some going on to a wall, others on to a window, and yet others going up on to the glass roof. The right-hand group, still keeping together, had migrated at the same time to the top of the creeper and from there on to the glass roof.

One thing puzzled us about all this: how the spiders lay down the silk along which they travel. For instance, the topmost leaf of the creeper is about one-and-a-half feet below the glass roof. From that leaf the silken path leaned obliquely up to the glass roof direct from the leaf. We know there are several ways in which the young spiders could have laid this track, apparently across thin air. One way would have been to let out their silken threads and allow them to be caught by any draught of air coming through the conservatory. These would be wafted about by the currents of air until they touched the glass and stuck to it. Once even one such strand had been secured it would be easy for all the spiders to swarm up it, each laying its own silken thread as it went, so broadening the pathway, making it stronger and giving a firmer foothold for those that followed. Another way would have been for one of the spiders to make its way from the leaf along a side twig touching the wall, thence up the wall and under the wooden framework of the roof of the conservatory, and along the glass to secure the thread at that point. Having done this it would take in the line it had laid down by jerking it free from the wall and the framework of the roof. Then it would take in the slack and pull the silk taut. We know spiders do use these methods but it is not often we have the good luck actually to see them do it. Whichever method was used, the fact remains that there was a silken thread passing from a leaf up through the air to the glass roof, and the right-hand group of spiders, unlike the left-hand group, were still clustered together, seven days after hatching. As I say, how they bridged the gap between the last leaf of the creeper and the roof of the conservatory is still a mystery. However it was done it must have called for some form of teamwork on the part of the young spiders, even if it was only the sort of teamwork that means keeping together and playing follow-my-leader.

Within twenty-four hours after this, the whole of the right-hand group had also dispersed to various points on the roof of the conservatory, and on the evening of the day of the 15th of May, that is, eight days after they were hatched, the one to two hundred young spiders, each no larger than a small pin's head, were dotted about all over the glass and wooden framework of the conservatory roof and along the tops of its windows.

Now we can go back and see what happened to the left-hand group. Three days before the right-hand group had finally dispersed, several of the spiderlings in the left-hand group had reached the framework of the glass roof and there each had spun its first snare. This was just a few strands of silk, laid down at random, but each of these irregular webs had been sufficient to catch two or three small insects, each insect being perhaps double the size of the spider that had made the web. Nevertheless, these insects had been shrouded with silk in the same way as the grown spider will do it, so although the young spiders were not yet capable of spinning a complete cartwheel web, they were able to handle their food.

I have dwelt at some length on the way the young spiders set out on their journey through life. It might almost seem that too much has been made of it since our subject is animal families. But it is not enough just to talk about the different kinds of families we find among animals. To make our story complete we ought to try to see what it is all about, and what is the importance of family life. That is where the young spiders can teach us a lot.

We are often told that spiders, and other animals like them, do everything from instinct. It is usual to put it this way: that wonderful as the web-spinning of spiders may be it is all instinctive. What this would mean is that spinning a web is very much like the wolf spider with her cocoon, where all she does is governed by changes taking place within her body. We know that all spiders belonging to one species will eventually spin the same kind of web. That we can see for ourselves. More than this, however, we are often told that the first web they spin is like the last, they do not have to learn how to spin it, and no matter how many webs they spin they show no improvement. That is, they learn nothing and are incapable of learning. As I say, that is what we are so often told; and I was anxious to see for myself whether it was, in fact, correct. That is why I was very glad to have been able to follow these young spiders on their journey. What I saw taught me a lot about the real meaning of family life, as we shall see.

Let us go back to the beginning. We watched this brood of young spiders up to the point where they were spinning their first webs. These, as we saw, were very simple affairs, composed of just a few strands of silk criss-crossing without order. The spiders were the young of the garden or diadem spider which builds those beautiful cartwheel webs we see so clearly when the autumn dews make them sparkle like jewels. There is a very big difference between that first simple web they spun and the beautiful cartwheel webs they would spin when they were older. So we find that the first part of the story as it is usually told us is not strictly correct.

When the young spiders were scattered all over the conservatory, we had plenty of opportunity to watch their progress day by day. Some of them made better progress than others, but in every instance the order of events was the same. At first they spun the simple web of criss-crossed threads. Then, perhaps the next day, or in some it was two or three days later, the silk threads became more regular so that they began to look like the spokes of a wheel. But although there were only a few spokes, we could see the real cartwheel web was being foreshadowed. Soon after the first webs began to assume the pattern of spokes, it was not long before a spiral thread was laid around them, and the web then began to look a little more like the orb-webs we know so well. Even so, the webs were all still very simple.

Day after day, each spider spun a new web. Some among them might miss a day now and then, using yesterday's web for a second day; but most of them spun a new web each day, and with each succeeding day the web showed an improvement on the last. The young spiders were rather like a small boy with his first penknife. He starts to whittle wood, and the first time he does this he ends up with a shapeless piece of wood. The next time, however, he does it a little more skilfully, and as he goes on he begins not so much to whittle as to carve. In it we see a pattern or design beginning to take shape.

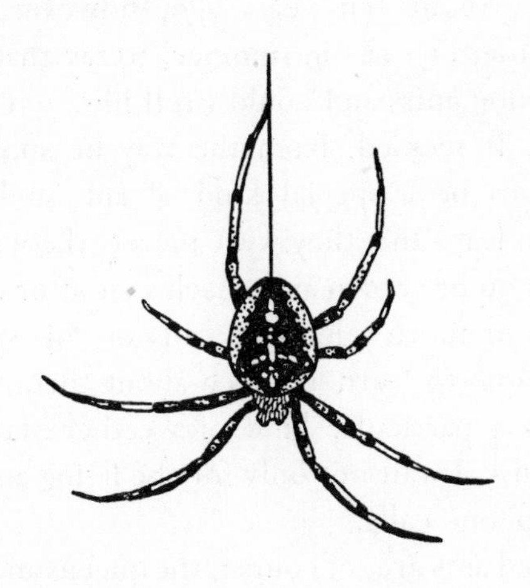

Insect Super-families

For some years now I have been taking particular note of flying ants. There is nothing special about this and I had seen them off and on every year of my life. About ten years ago, however, somebody telephoned me, one day in summer, to say that they had a swarm of flying ants, and could I tell him where they had come from. It seemed, from the way he spoke, that he took these to be a special kind of ant, and was quite interested to learn that they were merely the winged forms of the common or garden ants. Each year after this I would receive one or more telephone calls on this subject, so I felt it was time to learn as much about them as possible. Now, when a particular kind of weather sets in, about July or August, I wait not only for the flying ants, but also for the telephone calls.

The winged ants are, of course, the queens and the males.

The queens are not only winged but much larger than the worker ants, those we normally see running about the garden. The males are also winged but are only about the same size as the workers and therefore insignificant beside the large, conspicuous queens. That may be one of the reasons why, although we call the females queens, we do not call the males kings. Indeed, they are apt to be overlooked altogether. The workers are all sterile females, incapable of breeding. They are the drudges of the ant colony, and yet in some ways they dominate it, as we shall see.

The most favourable days for these swarms of winged ants to come out and take to the air are those that are sultry, with little wind. On such a day, either morning or afternoon, according to the conditions, they appear as if by magic, swarming first over the ground accompanied by large numbers of workers. There is no magic about it, however, and if you happen to dig out an ants' nest, or move a large stone under which a nest has been constructed, a week or a fortnight before the swarming, you will find large numbers of winged ants ready to come out. It is when I see these that I know the first sultry day will bring out the ants—and bring on the telephone calls.

We know that the flying ants come out when the weather conditions are just right. What we do not know is what exactly these weather conditions must be. As a rule, the swarming will take place only in certain areas or certain localities, on one particular day, but there have been rare occasions when ants have swarmed on the same day over the whole of England.

Although we do not know what are the right conditions, it seems that the worker ants do. For days, or even for a week or two beforehand, the winged queens and males are ready to set out on their nuptial flight, as it is called. Some people prefer to call it the wedding flight. When they are in this state of readiness, they are excited, constantly moving about inside the nest and even trying to get out. But until the weather is just right the workers restrain them from doing so. When the nest is under a large stone, it is possible, by lifting the stone carefully, actually to see this happening. They may be queens but they are compelled to obey the commands of their subjects.

When the appointed day arrives, and the weather is favourable, not only do the workers allow the winged ants to leave, they accompany them and, perhaps, if we knew the truth, lead them out. The first exodus brings winged and wingless ants out in a seething swarm on to the surface. At first glance all seems confusion. Yet, if we have the time and the patience to go down on one knee and watch, we soon see that there is less confusion than appeared at first sight. Certainly there is a lot of coming and going, but we soon begin to see that each queen is accompanied by a number of workers, perhaps a dozen to a score. As we continue to watch, these groups separate out from the mass and move off in different directions.

Every so often a queen will spread her wings and take off soon after coming above ground, leaving her attendant workers milling around as if distracted by her sudden departure. Others will go a short distance before taking off, but most of them climb on to a stone or some other high place—high in comparison to their size—before becoming airborne. The best sight we have of the departure of a queen is when she climbs a post. As she goes slowly up, the workers are fussing around her all the time. Some of them reach the top first and move to and fro as if impatient at the queen's slow pace. Once she arrives at the top it is not long before she spreads her wings and takes to the air. And once she has gone, the workers, after moving about fretfully for a while, descend the post and presumably go back to the nest.

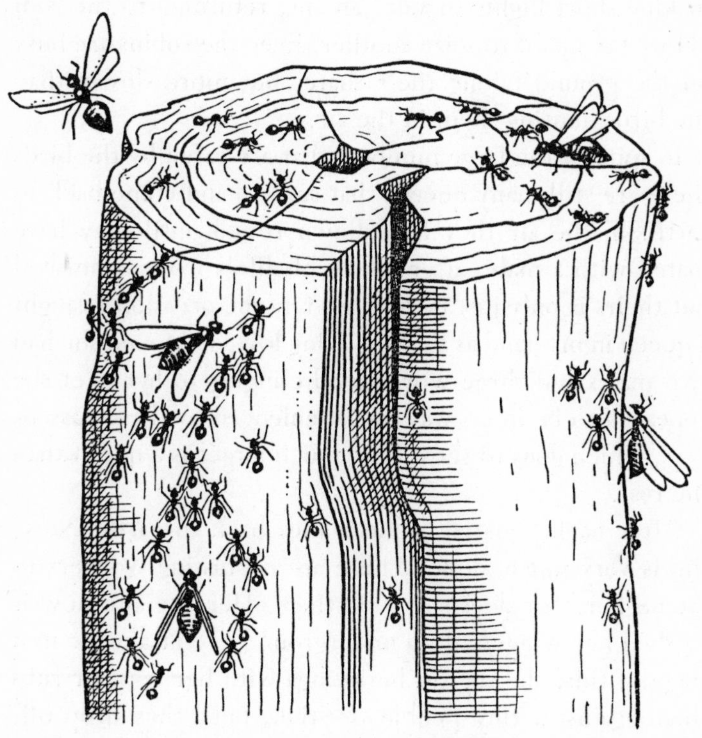

Queen ants climb to the top of a post escorted by workers, before setting off on their wedding flight

I presume they go back to the nest, for I have never troubled to follow them. The more exciting part to watch is the masses of winged ants now in the air. The males have also taken to the air but they are less easy to see. In a really good swarm the air seems filled with the flying insects, with birds busy among them. High overhead the swifts scream and wheel as they make the most of this harvest. Below them the swallows are darting to and fro and at a lower level the house-martins. At roof-top height starlings are making short flights to seize an ant, returning to the roof before taking off to seize another. Even the robins are busy on the ground taking their share, but more slowly than the birds hunting them in the air.

In spite of the large numbers that are eaten by the birds there are still many queens that survive and come back to earth. In the air they have flown round until they have mated with a male, after which his life's work is finished but theirs is only just beginning. On one occasion I caught a queen in my hand as she was flying low, and found she had two males and three workers all clinging to her. Yet she appeared to be in no way inconvenienced by these passengers, which goes to show how much larger is a queen than the rest.

After having mated a queen flies back to earth. Now, she is very much alone. There are no fussing workers to attend her, nor does she need them. Her one aim now is to shed her wings and go underground. To attain the first stage of this, she tugs at her wings with her legs, or rubs them against a tiny pebble or stick, until they drop off. At the end of the day, when all ants have gone below ground, we can see the wings littering the pavements and paths, irridescent useless things now. The queen needed them for one flight only.

If we use again the method of dropping on to one knee and watching, we can follow the movements of one of the queens. Wingless, she searches, examining a crack in a pavement, a tiny hole in the earth. She may go in and come out again a number of times before she finally disappears for the last time. We have little idea what is the meaning of the workers accompanying the queens, nor have we much idea what influences the queen in her choice of a hole to lead her to her future home. These and many other things represent problems still to be solved. We can only note what happens.

Before following the fortunes of the queen, let us see what happens to the males. We know that they do not return and the nearest I have come to knowing more than this occurred a few years ago. It had been a hot day and there had been a wonderful swarming of ants. As evening drew on I walked up on to some high ground, where a road led through some fields. There in the still evening air were groups of small winged insects, dancing in the rays of the setting sun. They were low enough that by reaching up I could catch several in my hand. They were the winged male ants. By the next morning they were gone. No doubt the bats had some, but the likelihood is that they had danced until exhausted, to fall finally to earth to die.

Meanwhile, the queens have gone underground, and to say exactly what happens there is not easy. The only way we can gain any idea, since it is impossible to follow them underground, is to catch one or more of the queens as they are trying to enter the earth and keep them in captivity. That is something for the expert, so we must now see what he has to say.

Underground the queen selects a spot for her future home, a small cavity maybe, or one which she perhaps enlarges a little. For the first days she must give her time to laying eggs, from which workers will hatch. She has no time to forage for food, but provision is already made for this. The muscles that worked her wings are no longer needed for this purpose and break down. The substance from her wing-muscles nourishes her body, and some of it is used also, in the form of her saliva, to feed the first grubs to hatch out. As soon as these few workers are fully adult they can take over the rest of the task of building the colony. This means tending the eggs and the grubs, enlarging the nest and foraging for food. These must be precarious days, when the workers are so few and the queen is already well under way with what will be henceforth her sole duty.

We are told that during these first days the queen may eat some of her own eggs. Whether this cannibalism is, as is sometimes suggested, a natural means of keeping herself alive, seems rather doubtful. It might easily be that, in the unnatural conditions under which, of necessity, we must keep her in order to study her, something happens to upset her, and that she behaves in consequence like the larger animals. On the other hand, it may, in fact, be the case that she does use some of her eggs as emergency rations.

The eggs are small, white and elliptical. The grubs hatching from them are legless and fairly helpless, and it is a month or more before they turn into pupae, and another three weeks before these are burst open and the first workers emerge. Taking the story up again at this point, we can follow some of the duties carried out by the workers. Everybody must have had the experience of breaking open an ants' nest, either by accident or design. The first thing we see is a mass of blackish bodies moving around in utter confusion. This is hardly surprising, since the event must have much the same effect on the ants as an earthquake has on a community of human beings. Within a very short while, however, we see that the eggs are being picked up and carried away, and it is not very long before these will have been taken to a place of safety.

Nature's law is the same as the unwritten law for human beings at sea, 'women and children first', or perhaps in the case of most animals the order is reversed. Certainly in ants the first care is for the eggs and cocoons, not only in the event of the catastrophe just described, but all the time. The eggs and grubs are constantly being licked by the workers, and the grubs are fed by the workers regurgitating food from their own crops into the mouths of the grubs.

One thing, it seems, helps the workers' attachment to their charges. Both eggs and grubs pass fluids through their outer surface which are attractive to the workers. That is, they like the taste of them. But this cannot be the sole reason for the care they show in looking after them, for always, whether we disturb them or whether an enemy attacks the nest, the growing infants, whether in the form of eggs, grubs or cocoons, are the first care of the workers. They move them about the nest from one chamber to another, according to the changes in temperature and humidity. What is more, at different stages the requirements of temperature and humidity vary. Eggs need one set of conditions, grubs another and pupae another, and as conditions within the colony change, as they do throughout the day, and from day to day, the workers move their charges round from one chamber to another. Thus they contrive to keep them all under the most favourable circumstances all the time, bringing them into the upper galleries of the nest in warm weather and carrying them down into the deeper galleries when the temperature falls.

Here, then, in ants we have what may be called a super-family. In it the males are short-lived, their sole task being to fertilize the queen. The workers, which may live for seven years, are unable to breed yet on them falls the burden of caring for the new generations, while the queen, who has been known to live for fifteen years, once her first trials are over, is fed by the workers and does nothing but lay eggs.

This is very much the situation we have in the well-known hive-bees and in the social wasps, both of which are related to ants. But these highly-organized communities, the super-families as I have called them, are found in relatively few of the more than a million known species of insects. In the great majority there is nothing approaching a family life, the eggs being laid and left to chance, the caterpillars or grubs hatching from them having to look after themselves.

There are two well-known exceptions to this, outside the ants, bees and wasps. The female earwig, when about to lay her eggs, digs a chamber just beneath the soil. There she broods her eggs and stays with the young earwigs after they have hatched. The shield bug lays her thirty or so eggs on the underside of a leaf. She also covers them with her body and remains in this position long after they have hatched. As the larvae grow they begin to move about, and at first the mother seems able to gather them together under her again, but before long they all move off to live on their own.

It is less easy to see how the earwig and the shield bug manage to keep their families together than it was with the cichlid fishes. Nor is it very clear what advantage the young insects gain, except that we know the mother earwig licks her offspring and keeps them clean of, at least, the spores of mildews. It might be that the shield bug larvae are hidden and thereby escape the attention of enemies. This is likely, as we know that the fully-grown shield bugs have a most unpleasant taste and most birds avoid them.

As we saw earlier, family life among birds and the higher animals includes not only the sheltering of the young but the feeding as well. Sometimes only one parent takes part, in other instances both do their share. Among insects, the males have nothing to do with their offspring once the eggs are laid. Such family life as there may be is the responsibility of the female.

Even when we have said all this, there is little that is haphazard in the early stages of the lives of insects. There is certainly less than in the many fishes that lay their eggs at random in the sea. There, the parents never see their offspring, except by accident, and the offspring never know their parents. It is completely the reverse of family life. This is also true of insects, yet some provision is made for the offspring. In summer we see the cabbage white butterflies swarming, and among them are the females ready to lay. Yet they do not lay their eggs on the first plant that presents itself, but, as their name suggests, deposit them on the leaves of cabbages or other related plants. In effect, the butterfly is anticipating the needs of the future caterpillar by laying the eggs on plants upon which it must feed.

This is, therefore, a form of parental care, in that the parent is doing something for the welfare of its offspring. It is not much, it is true, nor is it as obvious as in the earwig or shield bug, but it is at least a first step. The other important thing to note is that when we say the butterfly anticipates the needs of the caterpillar we do not mean that she thinks this out. Quite automatically, when about to lay her eggs, the female butterfly goes to the correct food plant. Why she does so would be difficult to say. It may be that the scent of the plant attracts her, possibly the colour or shape; or it may be all three. Whatever it may be, we can be sure that the butterfly's actions have nothing to do with taking thought for the future. It is important to realize this because, as we shall see, we can trace some kind of succession from the behaviour of the cabbage white butterfly to the wonderful super-families such as we have been considering. Although these super-families are so highly organized, and the members thereof seemingly so intelligent, there are few signs of a real ability to think. On the contrary, everything is carried out by a chain of automatic actions. A penny in a slot-machine brings forth a bar of chocolate. The smell (or sight) of a cabbage makes the cabbage white butterfly land and lay her eggs. This is true also for almost everything bees, wasps and ants do.

From giving shelter and no more, as in the shield bug, we can pass to insects that provide shelter for their offspring and anticipate their food requirements. One of the simplest examples is seen in the solitary wasps, known as sand wasps. The female sand wasp digs a vertical or sloping tunnel in the sand, which ends in a rounded chamber. She then goes off to hunt for food. This may be a caterpillar, fly or beetle, or it may be a spider; the different kinds of wasps select different victims. One of the commonest sand wasps in this country captures only smooth caterpillars. Having paralysed a caterpillar by stinging it several times, she drags it to the mouth of the burrow. She then goes

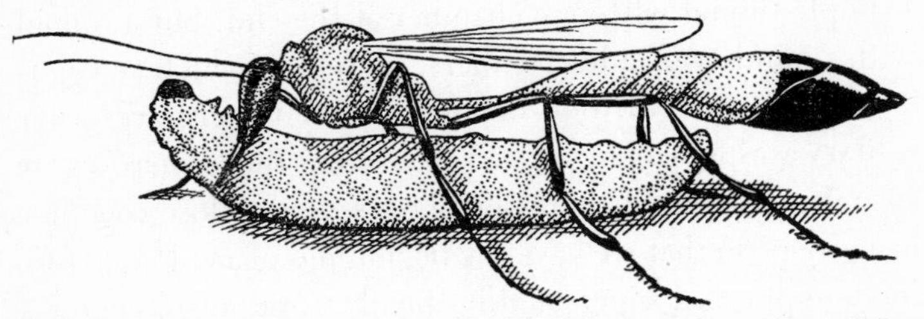

Hunting wasp dragging caterpillar to the burrow where she will lay her egg

down into the burrow to inspect it. If nothing has happened to it in her absence, she drags the paralysed caterpillar down into the chamber and there lays an egg on it. After this, she fills the shaft with sand and departs. Later, the egg hatches and the sand wasp larva feeds on the caterpillar, before pupating. Finally, it breaks out of the pupal skin and burrows its way to the surface, a fully-grown sand wasp. Another common sand wasp does much the same thing, except that after filling the burrow with sand it selects a large sand-grain and, holding this in its jaws, hammers the sand firmly into the mouth of the burrow.

There are other solitary wasps that dig burrows and lay eggs in them, but do not provision them beforehand. Such wasps go to find food for the larva as it hatches out. They also stand guard over the mouth of the burrow for a while, to keep enemies at bay. Other sand wasps continue taking food to the burrow after the larva has hatched, which comes even nearer to the way birds behave. And although it would be wrong to make too much of this, at least we can say that sand wasps are coming much closer to having a true family life.

The next step takes us to solitary wasps that dig not just a simple tunnel with one chamber at the end, but a tunnel with a number of side chambers, in each of which an egg is laid and a store of food deposited. Then there are other solitary wasps which, instead of making their burrows far away from those of their neighbours, build close together in a group, so that we have the beginnings of a colony. How the complicated super-families finally came into being is a very long story. All we can do here is to indicate some of the first steps.

Bees and wasps are, as we have seen, very closely related. One of the outstanding differences between them is that bees take vegetable food whereas wasps take mainly animal food. Otherwise there is much that is similar in their habits. Just as there are solitary wasps and colonial wasps, so there are solitary bees and colonial bees. The solitary bees do much the same as the solitary wasps, except that instead of provisioning their simple burrows with insect food, they use nectar and pollen. Again, just as some solitary wasps build burrows with several chambers, so we find some of the solitary bees doing much the same.

A good example of this is seen in the leaf-cutting bee. This is the one that cuts circular pieces out of the leaves of rose-bushes, and we can, if we keep watch, actually see the bee cutting the piece out and flying away with it held between its legs. It is not easy to follow the bee all the way, and usually we lose sight of it at this point. Then, one day, perhaps an old post is taken down, sawn up and split open, and we find the bee's nest. In a tunnel in the rotten wood we find what can best be described as a row of greenish-brown cigar stumps. Each is made of rolled pieces of rose leaf, covered at one end with a circular lid of the same material. Inside each are the remains of the store of pollen upon which the grubs fed.

There is another bee, found mainly in Southern England, that has a more complete family life, and comes much nearer to the honey-bees. The females appear in early spring, and each digs a vertical shaft in the ground, around which she excavates fifteen or more chambers. She fills these with pollen, lays an egg in each, and then seals them. After this she stays guard until the grubs hatch. These grubs eventually turn into female bees, like the mother except that they are smaller, are slightly different in appearance and cannot breed. They are, in fact, sterile females or workers. They take over from the female parent, whom we must now call the queen, the making of further brood-cells and the collecting of pollen to stock them. The queen now does nothing but lay eggs. By the time August arrives, there have hatched out young queens and also males, or drones. These mate, and soon after this the old queen, the drones and the workers, of which there were never more than about fifteen, die off. The young queens pass the winter in the parental burrow, and with the spring all leave except one, and she holds it by right of conquest. The other young queens go off to dig new burrows elsewhere.

Here, then, we have a colony that is almost a miniature of the colony of the hive bee, but in that there may be 60,000 workers instead of the fifteen, but the essential workings are much the same. The hive bee is really a domesticated animal, and has been kept by man for the last 4,000 years. Where it originally came from is uncertain, but it is believed to have come from India or from some place even further east. Certainly, its only known relatives are found wild in these regions, and the fact that hive bee colonies do not die off in winter, as do those of our native bees and wasps, strongly suggests that the bees are of tropical origin.

Here, again, we have the familiar story. The queen can do nothing but lay eggs. She cannot make the comb, nor collect food, and if left to herself her large family of grubs would die because she can neither feed them nor tend them. All these duties are carried out by workers, which are females unable to breed. In each cell built by the workers the queen lays one egg. This takes about three days to hatch. At first the grubs are fed on 'royal jelly', a special food given out by the workers, but later their diet is changed so that after the fourth day they receive pollen and honey. On the other hand, some grubs are destined to be queens, and these are fed on royal jelly all the time. The eggs from which future queens will hatch are larger than those giving rise to workers, and they hang bag-like from the comb. The males or drones also come from special cells, but these are like the worker cells except that they are larger.

When the population of workers in a hive becomes too great, a number of them leave in a swarm. The first swarm of the year is led by the old queen, a new queen taking her place as the head of the hive. This new queen leaves the hive, soon after the swarm has gone, on her marriage flight. Then she returns and settles down to do nothing but lay eggs. If there is a second swarm in the same year, it is headed not by a reigning queen but by a new queen.

In the bee hive the usual role of the offspring is reversed. Instead of being looked after by the parents, the parents, namely the queen and the drone, are tended by the numerous family.

Wasps form colonies very like those of the hive bees, but with important differences. In spring, the queen wasps, the sole survivors from last year, come out of hibernation and start looking for places to build their nests. They cannot give out wax as the hive bee workers do, and the nest as well as the cells in it are made of paper. The queen must chew old wood from gateposts, old trees and the like, mixing it with saliva to form wasp paper. Choosing a site inside a deserted mousehole, or other cavity well underground, she plasters a disc of paper on its ceiling. From the centre of the disc she next constructs a stalk, which widens out at the bottom end. Here the queen fashions a few six-sided cells into each of which she lays an egg. Then she builds an umbrella-like covering to protect these first cells. The grubs hatching from the eggs are fed on insects, previously masticated for the purpose. When they are fully grown they are the first workers in the colony, ready to take over the rest of the nest building. The umbrella-shaped covering is made larger until it forms a spherical or oval nest, and inside it more combs are made, all of paper. The queen goes on laying eggs, and each brood of workers hatched out adds to the labour force for finishing the building of the nest and for feeding and tending the larvae.

Towards the end of summer, special large cells are made, in which young queens are reared. Males also are hatched at this time, they and the queens being fed on special food. When the queens and males have mated that is the end of the colony. The males die off, the queens go into hibernation, the workers die off and the colony breaks down.

Although the hive bee is not native with us, we have others that are nest-builders, namely, the large bumble bees seen in March and April. These are the queens coming out of hibernation and seeking a place to make a nest. They search for the abandoned burrows of mice and voles. In them, each makes a round hollow nest of moss, leaves or fine grass. Some of the bumble bees, known as carder bees, plait these materials with their legs and jaws, making them into a nest hidden in the grass or coarse vegetation. Whatever the nest, the queen bumble bee places in it a paste of pollen mixed with honey. Around this she builds a cylinder of wax and lays within it a batch of eggs. She seals the cylinder with more wax and beside it, on the side nearest to the entrance to the nest, makes a waxen honey-pot and fills it with honey. The queen sits over the eggs to incubate them, leaving her post only to feed. Should the weather be bad she feeds from the honey-pot.

The eggs hatch in four days, and the white grubs feed on the paste inside the waxen cylinder. When they have eaten this, the queen makes a hole in the lid of the cylinder and, with her mouth, squirts a mixture of pollen and honey into the cell for the grubs to feed upon. Three weeks after the first eggs are laid the first workers come out of their cocoons. During that time, in addition to incubating the eggs and feeding the grubs, the queen has fashioned more cells and laid more eggs. Although the colony may eventually build up to the number of four hundred, the queen continues not only to lay eggs but to go out gathering food until there are enough workers to enable her to stay within the nest.

The rest of the story is like that of the other social bees and wasps native to this country. At the approach of cold weather in autumn, the young queens, who have already mated, go into hibernation. The old queens, the drones and the workers die off.

It is always the case that where we find industry and devotion to duty there will be found those ready to batten on it. The cuckoo unloads its burdens on the meadow pipit and the hedge-sparrow, and there are cuckoos among the bumble bees.

Among the cuckoo bees there are only drones and queens, and no workers. They impose themselves upon the hard-working bumble bees, eat their food, lay their eggs in the cells already prepared, and leave them to be tended by the workers. In the end, the rightful queen is stung to death, and only cuckoo eggs are laid. It is not difficult for this deception to be imposed since most of the cuckoo bees look very like the bumble bees they parasitize. Even so, they often do not get into the nests without a fight.

It has not been possible to do more here than sketch in very briefly what is known of the domestic affairs of bees, wasps and ants. Perhaps enough has been said to show how similar are their families, yet how different from those of other animals. One of the main differences is that their colonies are communities rather than families, and yet they are families in the sense that there is one mother, the head of the house, so to speak. In the ant colonies the likeness to communities is emphasized when we remember that some ants have their domestic animals (the greenfly), some go in for a kind of farming (growing small fungi for food), some keep slaves, go out on foraging expeditions to discover new sources of supplies, and wage war between themselves.

INDEX

Adder, 95
alligator, 92-4
ants, 134-42
anteater, giant, 79
Australian Teddy bear, 88

Baboons, 77-9
bandicoot, 86
bees, 142, 146-51
black-banded cichlids, 116-20
blackbird, 3-18, 27
blenny, 112
bullfinch, 37-41
bullhead, 105-6, 112
butterfish, 112
butterfly, 144

Caguan, 81
caiman, 92
cat, 37
centipede, 125-6
cichlids, 116-20
colugo, 81
coot, 35-6
crocodile, 92-4
crow, 46
cuckoo bees, 151

Darwin's frog, 99
dog-fox, see fox
ducks, 29-32, 44

Eagle, golden, 44
earwig, 142
elephant, 88

Flying lemur, 81
flying squirrels, 82
fox, 60-7
frog, 97-101

Giant anteater, 79
golden eagle, 44
grouse, 44
gulls, 36, 37

Hare, 72, 73
hedgehog, 49-58
hive-bees, 142

Kangaroo, 86-8
koala, 86

Lamb, 69
lemur, flying, 81
lizards, 95
long-tailed field-mouse, 70-5
lumpsucker, 112-14

Mallard, 29-32, 44

Index

marsupials, 86
merganser, 44
midwife toad, 101
Miller's thumb, 104, 105, 111, 112
monkeys, 79
moorhen, 33-5
mouse, 70-5

Native cat, 86

Opossum, 82-6

Pangolin, 81
partridge, 44
pheasant, 19-27
poison-frogs, 98
pouch-bearers, 86
python, 95

Rabbit, 71-3
rat, 75

Sand wasp, 145
scorpion, 125-6
sea-horse, 115
shrew, 73
sloth, 81
snakes, 95
sparrow, 41-3
spiders, 121-33
squirrels, 82
Stephens Island frog, 99
stickleback, 106-11
Surinam toad, 101-2
swan, 44, 45

Tadpole, 97
tamandua, 79-81
Teddy Bear, Australian, 88
toads, 98-101
tortoises, 95
tree frogs, 99
trumpeter swan, 45
turtle, 94

Vixen, 60-7

Wasps, 142-51
waterhen, 33-5
wolf spiders, 122-5
wombat, 86
woodcock, 45
wood-mouse, 70-5
wrasse, 112